DATE DUE			
Apr 10 '72			
Apr 24 '74			
May 8 '74			
May 21 '74			
Apr 7 78			

GAYLORD M-2   PRINTED IN U.S.A.

Man on the Moon

Man on the

The Impact on Science, Technology,
and International Cooperation

Basic Books, Inc., Publishers
New York   London

Edited by Eugene Rabinowitch
and Richard S. Lewis

The chapters in this volume appeared
in slightly different form in the
Bulletin of the Atomic Scientists.

© 1969 by Education Foundation for Nuclear Science

Library of Congress Card Catalog Number 76-94289

Manufactured in the United States of America

SECOND PRINTING

THE AUTHORS

Freeman Dyson is with the Institute for Advanced Study, Princeton, New Jersey.

Mose L. Harvey is Director of the Center for Advanced International Studies, University of Miami, and a former Senior Member, Policy Planning Council and Director, Office of Research for USSR and Eastern Europe, Department of State.

Sidney Hyman is a Fellow of the Adlai Stevenson Institute of International Affairs.

John A. O'Keefe is Assistant Chief, Laboratory for Theoretical Studies, Goddard Space Flight Center, Greenbelt, Maryland.

William Leavitt is Senior Editor of *Air Force Space Digest*, Washington, D.C.

Franklin A. Long is Vice-President for Research and Advanced Studies, Cornell University.

Sir Bernard Lovell, O.B.E., F.R.S., is Professor of Radio Astronomy and Director of the Experimental Station, Jodrell Bank, Nuffield Radio Astronomy Laboratories, University of Manchester, England.

Irving Michelson is Professor of Physics at the Illinois Institute of Technology.

Thornton Page is on leave from Wesleyan University as a scientific consultant to NASA's Manned Spacecraft Center.

Eugene Rabinowitch is Editor-in-Chief of the *Bulletin of the Atomic Scientists*.

Charles S. Sheldon II is Chief of the Science Policy Research Division of the Legislative Reference Service, Library of Congress, and its senior specialists in space and transportation technology.

Philip M. Smith is Program Director for Field Requirements and coordination in the Antarctic Program Office, National Science Foundation.

Sidney Sternberg is Division Vice-President and General Manager of the RCA Electromagnetic and Aviation Systems.

Ernst Stuhlinger is Associate Director for Science, Marshall Space Flight Center, Huntsville, Alabama.

Harold C. Urey is Professor-at-Large of Chemistry at the University of California, San Diego.

Wernher von Braun is director of the George C. Marshall Space Flight Center, Huntsville, Alabama.

AFTER THE LUNAR LANDING

Our concern in this volume is the impact upon science, technology and international cooperation of man's emergence from the "cradle," the biosphere of Earth, to visit the surface of another planet. The editors invited experts in the physical and social sciences who had been thinking, talking and writing about space programs for a long time. Some had been critical of manned space flight, its motives and its costs. Some have been or are currently involved in Project Apollo. Some had not committed themselves to value judgments but were fascinated by probable results.

In general, the authors regard the moon landing as a climactic event in man's evolution. Sir Bernard Lovell suggests it is likely to have a cataclysmic effect on society and that an international effort should be mounted to send men to Mars in the 1980s.

The question of how Project Apollo relates to a scheme of priorities which takes into account such needs as housing, health, pollution and the problems of urbanization enters the discussion from several points of view. Eugene Rabinowitch suggests that Apollo may stimulate the development of a system of establishing national priorities in the application of the nation's resources. Freeman Dyson, on the other hand, does not believe that any "hierarchy of committees" can devise an accepted order of priorities.

Ernst Stuhlinger proposes the idea that the scientific-industrial-social integration required to mount super-projects such as Apollo, and to carry them out within a predicted time frame may be the most important of the space program's results. It provides us with a technical know-how to deal with super-problems, such as trans-portation, the reclamation of our cities and countryside, pollution and food production and distribution.

Politically, the impact upon the Soviet Union of a first lunar landing by Americans is likely to shatter the "mystique" of Russian superiority in space technology, suggests Charles S. Sheldon II. But it may goad the Russian leaders into putting new infusions of money and talent into space projects. Mose L. Harvey forecasts that the drive of Soviet leaders to demonstrate prowess in space will accelerate, even as the American space effort is being cut back. He predicts that the Russians will orbit the first large, manned space station and fly the first re-usable space vehicle.

To Sidney Hyman, the political consequences of land-ing on the moon appear as in a cloudy crystal ball. In the long range, they can hardly be foreseen any more clearly than the consequences of the landing of Colum-bus on San Salvador 477 years ago.

The impact of the lunar landing on science and tech-nology appears to be more discernible than in any other field. Harold Urey sees in the arrival of man on the moon the prospect of collecting selenophysical data to resolve conflicting theories of lunar origin and evolution. It may then be possible to determine whether the moon origi-nated as a planet, like the Earth, and to gain a clearer view of the processes by which the solar system formed.

Irving Michelson looks back over the centuries to de-scribe the manner in which space-flight has transformed lunar studies from speculation to science. As an astrono-mer, Thornton Page suggests that most of the exciting new discoveries in astronomy are being made with space vehicles touring the solar system. John O'Keefe projects the impact of lunar exploration and related experiments on astrophysics and cosmology.

From a technological point of view, observes Wernher von Braun, the Apollo program has provided mankind with a deep space transportation system in only ten years. At this rate of development, the rocket pioneer predicts, voyages to the moon are only the beginning of manned excursion in the solar system.

Franklin A. Long has calculated the effect of Apollo on aerospace development and transportation technology and Sidney Sternberg describes how automated checkout and monitoring systems, developed for Apollo, may be applied to the whole spectrum of industrial production.

So the discussion begins. It will not end in our time.

Eugene Rabinowitch
Richard S. Lewis

CONTENTS

PART I

THE MOON AND MAN

SIR BERNARD LOVELL, O.B.E., F.R.S.

1. MAN MOVES INTO THE UNIVERSE

Through the evolutionary processes of a billion years man has developed as a prisoner of the planet Earth. His physical condition has been determined by the parameters of a planet with a mass of 6×10^{24} kilograms, and a radius of 6378 kilometers. He has evolved with the consequent force of gravity—giving a surface acceleration of 982 cm/sec²—as a naturally occurring determinant of his movements. On Venus these physical conditions are similar, with a surface acceleration of 850 cm/sec². Yet man evolved on Earth but not on Venus. For reasons which we do not yet understand the atmosphere of these two planets developed in totally different directions, on Earth in a manner which enabled life to replicate and support itself, but on Venus in a way which is quite hostile to any forms of life known to us.

BREAKING OUT

Although the atmosphere of Earth has developed in a favorable direction for the support of life, it has also made man like a prisoner in a nearly dark cell. We have merely glimpsed the external world beyond Earth because our only sensors to this external environment have been our eyes and they have been sensitive only to the small range of electro-magnetic radiation which can penetrate the atmosphere. It is true that during the last few decades of our long history we have also been able to study the universe in another part of the electro-magnetic spectrum—the radio-wave region. The discoveries made in so short a time with equipment which must still be elemental in the context of future history have been shattering in their impact on our knowledge of the external world.

Now, suddenly man has emerged from these physical constraints. On October 4, 1957, he created his first artificial satellite—a demonstration that, in the future, the obscuration of the Earth's atmosphere need present no barrier to the study of the totality of the radiations coming from outer space. Then on April 12, 1961, in the person of Yuri Gagarin, man freed himself from the physical constraints of this planet. In the years which followed, many men clearly demonstrated that there were no physical or psychological barriers to existence in a different gravitational environment and that man could live and think for weeks in a state of weightlessness.

Now, so quickly, and before human society has been able to absorb and adjust itself to these newly found abilities, an entirely new dimension has been created. Men are moving to the moon and its vicinity, surviving and working under a gravitational field only one-sixth that of Earth, on an arid landscape without any local atmosphere to protect them from the alternate heat of the sun or cold of interplanetary space.

It has been common in our age to talk of revolutionary developments. Indeed there have been many in the fields of communication, transport, and in the medical and surgical treatment of individuals. But these, and all the discoveries in the whole of man's history, have had to be contained within the framework of the planet. Our thought and life have been monopolized by the struggle to adjust and live with their impact in a local terrestrial sense. We have observed and admired the universe; now we have begun to move into it in a decisive manner. It is a movement which is revolutionary in a sense which has never before occurred in man's history.

IMPACT ON SCIENCE

In the excitement of the tremendous accomplishment it is easy to overlook the deep implications of the achievement for the future of man. It is indeed a great misfortune that many individuals have looked upon Apollo in the manner of a stunt for national aggrandizement and have pleaded that the money should be diverted to what they imagine to be more important human requirements. It is hard to be sympathetic with such a viewpoint from any aspect. Materially, the annual cost of Apollo is less than 15 per cent of that of the current war, and the science budget which supports the entire space program is a few per cent only of the gross national product. Socially, Apollo may have a cataclysmic effect on terrestrial society. Some of these reactions are easy to foresee; others are buried in the future and entwined with man's own reaction to the good and evil which are contained within all new science and technology.

It is for example fairly easy to foresee the impact of Apollo on terrestrial science. There is, first, the science of the moon itself, and second, the use of the moon for scientific research. The first of these is of such great astronomical importance that it could be held to justify the whole space program. Broadly speaking there are two unsolved major problems which determine the trend of astronomical research. One is the attempt to understand how the universe came into existence and how it evolved; the other is the attempt to understand the origin and evolution of the solar system. The latter problem will be almost instantly elevated to new levels of understanding, if not solution, by Apollo. So far man's only access to extra-terrestrial material has been the meteorites. But their origin is uncertain and they are in any case modified by their passage through the Earth's atmosphere. Now we have access to lunar material. The moon has no atmosphere; its surface features have not been molded by weather conditions like the Earth's. The entire four-and-a-half billion years of the geological history of the solar system are contained in the lunar material, modified only by the natural evolutionary features which we seek to uncover.

Whenever science seems on the verge of a decisive investigation, so frequently those results uncover new perplexities. The analysis of the lunar material will no doubt do this—already without any landings the existence of the mascons was discovered—but at least a new set of queries can be asked and answered as the Apollo program develops. It is a reasonable supposition that an immediate result of these investigations will be a severe constriction on the range of arguments about the origin of the moon. Did it accrete separately during the formation processes of the whole system or is it the partial disintegration of a larger body which formed initially from the primeval material of the solar system? The settlement of this problem will, in turn, narrow the range of possibilities for the development of the whole planetary system.

A BASE FOR RESEARCH

There have been arguments that man is unnecessary for these investigations and that the lunar samples could be returned to Earth by automatic means. It may be conceded that there is force in that argument if the science of the moon was the only point at issue. But man is essential to pursue the second major consequence of Apollo which will be the initiation of the moon as a base for scientific research. The instantaneous benefit here will be to the astronomical sciences. Our knowledge of the universe has been achieved in the narrow optical and radio regions of the spectrum. To observe even in these parts of the spectrum without the hindrances to seeing introduced by the Earth's atmosphere and ionosphere is an astronomer's dream. But the moon as a base opens the entire spectrum. The recent short duration observations in rockets of X-rays from the universe, for example of the pulsar in the Crab nebula, is a sample of the rich harvest awaiting the astronomer.

SOVIETS ON THE MOON

The low gravitational field of the moon and the absence of wind and weather remove many of the problems which confront the engineer in his attempt to build large optical and radio telescopes of high accuracy on Earth. Hence, in these already highly sophisticated techniques the moon as a base will become a major influence in astronomical research as soon as the transport of significant amounts of material becomes a possibility. In the other parts of the spectrum where the receiving devices are already carried in the nose cones of rockets or in Earth satellites there seems no reason to delay an early installation on the lunar surface.

One of the tragedies of the last decade is the failure of the great powers to achieve any measure of cooperation in the lunar flights. In fact, in America at least, it has been regarded as a race with the Soviets. To what extent this has been based on reality is certainly open to question but the fact is that the crash-landers, the soft-landers and the orbiters have duplicated one another in time and content. Now the world is presented with another great opportunity for collaboration in the organization of the lunar-based researches. Man must either proceed immediately to organize these on an international basis or suffer the consequences of international rivalry on the moon. It is not hard to see how trouble can develop. The Soviets will clearly be on the moon themselves in the near future. If they deposit their own apparatus, which transmits on their own chosen frequencies in default or defiance of any international regulations, chaos will quickly develop. Apollo has opened a vast domain for peaceful researches on the great problems of the universe. The realization of this opportunity demands the immediate creation of a supranational authority to control the lunar bases, and to receive and process the data telemetered to Earth. For a short time the American nation is in a superior lunar position and it is to the American scientists and politicians that the world must now look for the initiatives on this vital matter. It is, of course, true that the outer space treaty already extant negates claims to sovereignty in outer space, but much more positive action is required to organize and control the lunar researches. Otherwise this supreme effort of man will become clouded in confusion and bitterness. It is easy to declare neutrality but hard to achieve its practical realization on Earth. On the moon it will become utterly impossible unless the problem is grasped now.

A MARS MISSION

The success of Apollo also demands international collaboration for an entirely different reason. There are no longer technical or physiological reasons why man should not soon begin the program of development necessary to send human beings to Mars. It will be expensive, but technically a human landing on Mars in, say 1980–85, is probably more realistic than the 10-year scale for the moon landing was in 1961; the history of our age shows that neither the Soviet Union nor America is likely to be deterred by cost when such a technical possibility occurs. Indeed, from the cost aspect, the Mars lander might well serve as an almost tailor-made take-up for U.S. industry and technology if Vietnam hostilities cease. The annual costs of the war and the planetary program are probably not dissimilar.

The scientific reasons for a manned Mars expedition are, of course, immense. All the arguments about the significance of lunar science apply again. In fact the Martian geological studies may be the only means of proceeding with the solution of the problems left over after the lunar analysis. Added to this are the whole range of biological issues presented by Mars. If replicating organisms are found to exist in the atmosphere or on the surface of the planet, unqualified support would thereby be produced for the belief that widespread development of organisms has occurred elsewhere in the universe.

CONTAMINATION DANGER

The immense importance of this issue demands that the world as a whole should share the responsibility for the investigation. Contamination by human species, or by earlier rockets or satellites before the manned flights, could prejudice the entire investigation. The Soviets have not, so far, expressed their agreement with the standards suggested by the National Aeronautics and Space Administration and the Committee on Space Research of the International Council of Scientific Unions. Indeed their planetary technique, as exhibited by their investigations of Venus, allows the carrier bus to plunge to destruction in the planet's atmosphere.

The urgency of renewing attempts at a clear international understanding on these investigations arises also because of the danger of contamination on Earth by returning manned planetary probes. Even though the moon is an arid body, the Apollo program involves strict quarantine arrangements for the returning astronauts. The risks of contamination are probably negligible; nevertheless NASA has quite rightly taken every reasonable safeguard. With Mars the risk must be far greater. The only safe assumption to make is that a spacecraft returning from Mars would probably convey entirely foreign organisms to the terrestrial environment. The consequences could be disastrous to crops or animal life unless the necessary controls can be exercised. This is manifestly an international problem, and international agreement is essential on the biological investigations to be made before a manned flight is attempted, and on the quarantine and other biological safeguards to be applied to the returning spacecraft.

MAN ON MARS

Finally, it is interesting to observe that, since man has demonstrated the possibility of existence on the moon, once he gets there man can certainly live on Mars. He will feel more normal than on the moon since the surface gravity on the planet is nearly one-third of that on Earth. Furthermore the planet has an atmosphere, which although probably largely nitrogen, certainly contains oxygen and water vapour. The atmospheric pressure at the surface is only one-twelfth of that on Earth but at 31 kilometers altitude the pressure on Mars and Earth are the same. Most important too is that, although the planet is rather cold, the Martian temperatures are in the habitable terrestrial range—probably ranging from 200 to 300 degrees absolute. Under these favorable initial conditions the development of a terrestrial technology capable of transporting men to Mars could probably devise a technique for the engineering of the Martian atmosphere to make it capable of life support in the normal sense. If some of the gloomy prognostications about the future of life on Earth have any substance then the terrestrial conditions in the twenty-first century may demand the permanent transfer of human colonies to Mars to insure the survival of the species. This futuristic problem transcends national boundaries. Unfortunately the success of Apollo today means that instant international action is required if the future of Mars is not to be jeopardized.

Although in size and mass Venus bears greater similarity to Earth than to Mars, it is hardly likely to be the target for other than purely scientific measurements by unmanned probes. Radio and radar measurements from Earth and space probe measurements by the American Mariner spacecraft and the Russian Veneras which deposited capsules into the atmosphere have shown that the planet is exceedingly hostile. The surface temperature is in the region of 700 degrees absolute and the atmosphere is largely carbon dioxide at extremely high pressure.

Will these planetary concepts remain speculative ideas although manned landings on Mars may be technically feasible within two decades? Oddly enough the answer probably depends on the development of the relations between the Soviet Union and America during the next five to 10 years. Historically, America was in a relatively poor scientific and technical condition for the decade immediately following World War II. It was the Sputnik of 1957 which delivered the shock of Soviet achievement and led to the total rethinking of the investment in American science and education. Then the continued superiority of the Soviets in space was the irritant which stirred President Kennedy to his "sail this new ocean" speech of 1961 and hence directly to Apollo.

A NEW TREND

The reaction has already set in. The budget of NASA has had a decreasing trend, too many of the space programs for 1970–75 have been cut and too many influential voices are raised against the investment level of the space program. It seems unlikely that the success of Apollo will in itself reverse this trend to the extent that is desirable. In this case it seems most probable that American space technology will become inward-looking: that is, the developments will have an essential terrestrial bias—communications, world resources, navigation, meteorology and possibly terrestrial transport with recoverable and re-usable space ships.

On the other hand if the Soviet-American relationship remains cool and shrouded in suspicion, implying a continued secrecy in the Soviet space programs, then the 1957 Sputnik era could repeat itself at a higher level. No one seems certain what the Soviets are doing in space. The most likely guess is that they are proceeding with the Earth-rendezvous concept for the build-up of a large orbiting space platform with a ferry service from Earth. This would give them an important military-space advantage, and an orbiting base for space science and launching of men and material to the moon and planets. The success of Apollo may well impel the Soviets to greater efforts in these directions which will become manifest in 1970–75 just as the U.S. space program feels the unfortunate effects of the current downward trend in its budget. This situation, which seems to have every prospect of developing, could, within the next few years, create another 1957–1961 space atmosphere in the United States, this time leading to a manned planetary program.

Thus we seem to be faced with a peculiar dilemma. In the sphere of man's intellectual development Apollo could mean lunar bases for science within 10 years and manned investigation of Mars within 20 years. Success in both enterprises demands collaboration between the

Soviet Union and the United States. A consequence of such collaboration could well remove the competitive instinct, based on fear, which alone might stimulate the individual governments to finance the huge scientific and technical developments involved.

In whatever way these trends develop it is certain that Apollo has marked an epoch for mankind of a type never before encountered. In the field of science an entirely new era of lunar-based astronomy and physics has been opened. A human adventure of unprecedented magnitude has been undertaken, in which a single nation's science and technology encompassed in a vast management and organizational framework has been stretched to achieve the almost impossible.

FREEMAN DYSON

2. HUMAN CONSEQUENCES OF THE EXPLORATION OF SPACE

When Columbus set sail into the Atlantic, he knew he was going to do something great, but he did not know what. This remark about Columbus is trite. It has been made a hundred times before by people discussing man's activities in space, yet it is the truest thing that can be said. In my personal view of the human situation, the exploration of space appears as the most hopeful feature of a dark landscape. Everything I say may well be as wrong and irrelevant as Columbus' reasons for sailing West. The important thing is that he did sail West and we do go into space. The true historical consequences of these events can only be known much later.

In recent months many thoughtful voices have been heard, questioning the wisdom of pursuing big space projects at a time when so many human problems remain unsolved on earth. Just now, when the direction of space activities after the Apollo missions is still to be decided, it is important for us to think seriously about the value of such enterprises. This article is an attempt to think ahead, to sketch a possible future for man in space. My intention is not to make my readers believe everything I say, but to provoke them into forming their own judgments, their own visions of human needs and purposes.

I do not think we need to have a generally agreed set of goals before we do anything ambitious. I do not believe that any philosopher-king or hierarchy of committees can dissolve the causes of human discord and give us a universally accepted order of priorities. On the con-

trary, I consider it natural and right that we shall continue to stumble ahead into space without really knowing
why. The ultimate strength of the space program derives
from the fact that it unites in a constructive effort a
crowd of people who are in it for quite diverse reasons.
I am in it partly because I am a scientist and am interested in astronomical problems. But many scientists are
indifferent or hostile to the program, while I myself was
enthusiastic about space travel long before I became a
scientist.

THE HUMAN SIDE

I shall be expressing opinions about matters which are
much more human than scientific. I shall put forward a
point of view about the social problems of our time, problems which have little to do with science or with space.
At the end I will argue that the exploration of space
offers remedies to some of our social diseases, but my
argument will remain on the level of literature rather
than of science.

When I am discussing human affairs, I like to deal in
individual people rather than in abstract principles. For
this reason I find science fiction more helpful than soci-
ology in suggesting probable futures. Like anybody who
is concerned with the long-range future, I owe a great
debt to the ideas of H. G. Wells. Wells was an unsuccessful biologist who became a successful novelist. He
understood better than most of us the comedy of the
individual human being, and yet he never lost sight of
his biological background, of the human species emerging from dubious origins and groping its way to an even
more dubious destiny. He was no physicist, and he never
took space travel seriously, although he used it on occasion as a stage property for his stories. His visions of
man's future are earthbound, pessimistic, and quite different from my vision as I shall describe it to you shortly.
But I do not need to agree with Wells in detail in order
to acknowledge the greatness of his influence. I take his
contribution to human thought to be not the description

of particular futures, but the awareness of the future as an object of intellectual study, having a depth and breadth as great as the study of the historic past. I am a child of Wells insofar as I cannot think of human destiny beyond the year 2000 as lying outside the scope of my responsibilities.

As an example of the sort of insight into human character that I find more illuminating than sociological analysis, let me mention the Artilleryman who appears briefly in Wells' *War of the Worlds*. This is an insignificant man who becomes convinced, as civilization collapses around him, that he can keep everything under control. He has unlimited self-confidence and a fine flow of words, quite out of touch with reality. Recently I met a U.S. diplomat who serves in a country where our policies might charitably be described as being on the point of collapse. At first I wondered, "Now where have I met this man before?"—and then I remembered Wells' Artilleryman. If you listen carefully, you will hear the voice of the Artilleryman wherever human society is facing problems of overwhelming difficulty.

Another splendid example of Wells' insight is the General Intelligence Machine which appears in his story *When the Sleeper Wakes*, written in 1899. It did not take much wisdom to foresee in 1899 a machine which would sit in somebody's living room and speak upon request, giving up-to-date news reports concerning the events of the day. Wells' insight is shown in the nature of the information which the machine provides. It puts out a continuous stream of advertising commercials and political propaganda, at such a level of imbecility that the characters in the story refer to it only by the name of "Babble Machine." To give the flavor of the thing, I quote directly from Wells: "Babble Machines of a peculiarly rancid tone filled the air with strenuous squealing and an idiotic slang, 'Skin your eyes and slide,' 'Gewhoop, bonanza,' 'Gollipers come and hark!'" I find it comforting, when the drivel put out by our contemporary Babble Machines drives me to fury or despair, to reflect that even the worst television commercials are not quite as bad as Wells imagined they would be.

FACTS OF LIFE

Let me give you a short list of facts which I regard as central to the human situation. Like Wells and other social analysts, I shall select my facts to make my theory plausible.

One fact of human life which is hard to ignore is nationalism. In all parts of the world nationalism is the strongest political force. In most places it is the only effective force making possible the organization of man's efforts for peace or war. Where nationalism is weak, as in Nigeria or Belgium, it is usually because a smaller political unit—a tribe or a province—has usurped the place of the nation in men's minds. The strength of nationalism in the world as a whole has steadily increased during recent centuries, and is probably still increasing.

Another obvious fact of life is race. The events of the last years have made it clear, if it was not clear before, that the problem of race runs deep in our society. No society with a substantial racial minority is free from problems. Some societies are more tolerant than others, but tolerance is fragile. For most of us it is pleasanter to live segregated than to face the frictions of racially mixed housing. In the pure-white English society into which I was born, having at that time no Negroes to worry about, we developed our famous class system instead. As a middle-class child, I was unable to communicate with most of the children of my neighborhood, since they were "Oiks" and spoke a different dialect.

A third fact of life is drugs. By this I mean not the harmless legal drugs like aspirin and penicillin, but the illegal ones, LSD, marijuana and so forth. Many people no doubt have more experience with these than I do, but at least I have not brought up a couple of teen-agers without realizing that drugs are an important part of the landscape. And it is clear to me that the existing drugs are only the first wave of an ever-increasing series of problems which may be included under the general heading of biological experimentation. As biochemistry advances there will be more varied drugs, illegally available, offering strange adventures to reckless young people. To make these legal will never be acceptable to anxious parents and neighbors; to make them illegal will never effectively stop their abuse. Later on, when biology and genetics have advanced a little further, even more serious problems of medical experimentation will arise. Our young people may be able to induce dreams and hallucinations in each other, programmed to order, by gadgetry feeding directly into the brain. What reality would be able to compete with this dream-world for their minds? Ultimately, perhaps a hundred years from now or perhaps sooner, humanity will be faced with the possibility of deliberate programming of the genetic make-up of children. Either a government using its paternalistic authority, or a group of individuals in defiance of authority, may cause children to be born differing radically from the norm in moral or intellectual power. Such experimentation may be of immense value from certain points of view. What a grand and terrible thing it would be to call into being a child with the endowments of Einstein or of Martin Luther King! And yet, which of our existing social institutions is strong enough to withstand the stresses that a generation of genetic experimentation would produce?

I have listed three disagreeable facts that confront the human species, the facts of nationalism, racism, and biological engineering. Under the heading of biological engineering I include the whole range of problems of which LSD gives us a foretaste. These three facts are usually regarded as separate problems, each to be handled as best we can in its own context. I shall instead concentrate attention on the features common to all three, and see if there is perhaps some underlying pattern.

PEOPLE IN SMALL GROUPS

I find the underlying pattern to be the propensity of human beings to function best in rather small groups. We are almost all familiar with the happiness that comes from a communal effort. Goethe has described it imperishably in the death scene of his "Faust." Our teen-agers are disoriented because they are no longer involved in the communal activities of family and village, sowing and harvesting, hedging and ditching.

Our pot-smoking teen-agers are unanimous in saying that the great thing about pot is not the drug itself but the comradeship which it creates. And to make the comradeship real, there must not only be a group of friends inside the circle but enemies outside, police and parents and authorities to be defied. Just so, in the old Yorkshire wool factory, the spirit among the workers was warm and intimate, not in spite of but because of their shared hostility to the mill-owner and his managers. This is human life the way it is: my son wearing his hair odiously long just because I dislike to be seen together with it in public, and we of the older generation fulfilling our duty as parents by keeping our hair short and marijuana illegal.

I believe the strength of nationalism and racism derives ultimately from the same source as the tension between the generations. We all have a psychological need to feel identified with a group, preferably not too large a group, with a common purpose and a common enemy. Countries like the United States are already far too big to fulfill this need satisfactorily. Small countries like Holland and Switzerland can generally handle social problems better than big ones. Nationalism is most triumphantly successful in countries which are both small and threatened, such as Finland, Israel, North Vietnam and Biafra.

GENETIC DRIFT

It is easy to theorize, as many paleontologists have theorized, that the human species has built-in instincts of tribal exclusiveness, frozen into our inheritance during the hundreds of thousands of years which our ancestors spent roaming in small nomadic bands. Such a theory is plausible as an explanation of present-day nationalism, racism and teen-age gang warfare, but I do not know whether it can ever be proved. For my purposes it is not important to decide whether exclusiveness is an inherited instinct or a culturally acquired characteristic. The important thing is that tribal exclusiveness exists in our species and has been essential to our rapid evolution.

Rapid evolution in any species depends largely on a phenomenon known as "genetic drift." Genetic drift is the random drifting of the average genetic make-up in a small inbreeding population. The speed of drift varies inversely with the square-root of the size of the breeding-group. The direction of drift is somewhat influenced by natural selection, but drift occurs even in the absence of selection. It seems to me incontestable that a group of apes could develop an aptitude for calculus, or symphonic music, or theological argument, only through genetic drift and not through natural selection. In fact all the things which we prize most in human culture, our appreciation of art, poetry, holiness and natural beauty, must be products of genetic drift.

I believe, though this is pure speculation, that genetic drift has been of decisive importance to human progress even in historic times. When we make a list of the most creative periods in human history, confining ourselves to the Christian-European tradition with which I am familiar, we think immediately of eighth-century Jerusalem, fifth-century Athens, and fourteenth-century Florence. In each case we have a city, hardly more than a village by modern standards, producing out of a small population within a hundred years an astonishing concentration of intellectual achievement. In each case the outburst of genius followed a long period during which the city existed with an even smaller population, rather isolated from its neighbors and quarreling with them incessantly. It seems to me plausible that the best recipe for human cultural progress would read roughly as follows: Take a hundred city-states, each with population between ten and a hundred thousand; let each one hate its neighbors sufficiently to prevent substantial interbreeding; encourage priestly and aristocratic caste systems to reduce still further the size of breeding units; introduce an occasional major war or plague to keep the populations small; let the mixture simmer for a thousand years, and maybe one of your hundred cities will be the new Florence, the new Athens, or the new Jerusalem.

FORCES OF TECHNOLOGY

So far I have presented the case for human divisiveness, for insularity, exclusiveness and intolerance. I want to make clear that these human qualities, however evil their consequences in our present society, are not easily to be eradicated. Throughout the long centuries of our pre-history and even until quite recently, these qualities have been beneficial to our species. In the self-sacrifice of a soldier, the fury of a mob, the loyalty to his friends of a teen-ager, the same qualities are still with us. We still function best in small groups.

Now we are all well aware that this is only half the story. We cannot go back to the Middle Ages or to classical Greece, even if we wished to. The idea of universal human brotherhood may still be remote for most of us. But against the historic forces of tribalism stand the three great forces of modern technology, the forces of weaponry, population growth and pollution. We are in danger of exterminating ourselves with our hydrogen bombs and the still worse horrors with which biological engineering will soon provide us. We are in danger of exhausting our resources and ultimately reducing ourselves to a starvation diet through over-population. We are in danger of ruining all that is beautiful on this planet through our accumulations of poisonous mess. All three dangers demand that mankind unite. Each of them, and the problem of weapons above all, requires a worldwide authority to protect us from our own folly. Slowly and against stubborn resistance, practical necessities are driving us to forget our quarrels and accept peaceful coexistence with our enemies. For 24 years the nuclear physicists have been saying "One world, or none," and there is no reason to doubt that in the long run they are right. The Earth has grown too small for bickering tribes and city-states to exist on it. Our bombs are too big, our machines are too complicated, our smog and garbage are too pervasive to be left much longer in the hands of local authorities.

As far into the future as any one can see, the dangers of modern technology will continue to grow and will threaten mankind on this planet with the choice of political union or death. Political union will inevitably mean some degree of political oppression, government by remote bureaucracy, over-centralization. We will be lucky if we can succeed in organizing a world government which does not degenerate into a world police state. But I believe the forces of tribalism and nationalism will for a long time remain strong enough to defeat attempts to impose world government. Men will prefer to live in filth with the threat of annihilation hanging over their heads, rather than allow foreigners to tax them.

Unfortunately the unifying force of technology, while not yet powerful enough to bind us into a world-wide brotherhood, is already quite strong enough to destroy the historic benefits which we once derived from tribalism.

THE HOPE OF SPACE

Now I come at last to the hopeful part of my message. I have presented a gloomy view of our human predicament. On the one hand, we are historically attuned to living in small exclusive groups, and we carry in us a stubborn disinclination to treat all men as our brothers. On the other hand, we live on a shrinking and vulnerable planet which our lack of foresight is rapidly turning into a slum. Never again on this planet will there be unoccupied land, cultural isolation, freedom from bureaucracy, freedom for people to get lost and be on their own. Never again on this planet. But how about somewhere else?

I believe in fact that space-travel does provide an answer to many of these grave human problems. The only question in my mind is "When?" Many of you may consider it ridiculous to think of space as a way out of our difficulties, when the existing space program, such as it is, is being rapidly cut down, precisely because it appears to have nothing to offer to the solution of social problems. It is of course true that the existing space program has nothing to offer. If one believes in space as a major factor in human affairs, one must take a very long view.

A SHARP DISTINCTION

To avoid misunderstanding, I would like to emphasize again that I am making a sharp distinction between human affairs and scientific affairs. The existing space program consists of two very unequal parts, the scientific program using unmanned vehicles and absorbing about one-tenth of the money, and the unscientific program including manned flights and taking nine-tenths of the money. The scientific program has already been of immense value to science. In the next two decades, if the economy axe has not chopped it to pieces, the scientific space program should be able to settle the question of the existence of life on Mars, and I cannot think of any question in the whole of science more important than that. In the long run the discovery of alien life would undoubtedly have human as well as scientific consequences, but I do not include these in my discussion. I am looking for consequences of space travel that affect the mass of my fellow citizens and not merely my academic colleagues. The unscientific part of the existing space program affects the public more directly but only superficially. It is in essence an international sporting event with the whole world as spectators. I am a supporter of the manned space program for reasons which I will presently explain, but I do not pretend that it yet offers benefits commensurate with its cost, either to science or to the general public.

How long it will take for space travel to become socially important is mainly a matter of economics, a field in which I have no competence. I will only put forward a few tentative remarks to suggest that the time should be measured in decades rather than in centuries. There is a prevalent view among the educated public that space travel is necessarily and permanently so expensive that it can never be made available to large masses of people. I believe this view to be incorrect. An interesting analysis of the economics of our existing space operations was made by Theodore Taylor ("Propulsion of Space Vehicles" in Marshak, "Perspectives in Modern Physics," Interscience, 1966). He calculated the cost of running a commercial jet-plane service from New York to Los Angeles under the following ground rules: (1) There shall be no more than one flight per month. (2) The airplane shall be thrown away after each flight. (3) The entire costs of Kennedy and Los Angeles airports shall be covered by the freight charges. Under these rules, which are the rules governing our present space program, the cost of freight between New York and Los Angeles is comparable to the cost of putting freight into orbit. The point of this calculation is that the economies of commercial airline operations are economies of scale and of efficient organization. There is no basic physical or engineering reason why it should be enormously cheaper to fly to Los Angeles than to fly into orbit.

I will not go here into a technical discussion of the problems of space propulsion. In order to make space travel cheap we need two things. The first is a reliable vehicle, preferably an air-breather, which can take off from an airport, fly itself directly into orbit, re-enter and land, and be ready to repeat the operation day after day. The second is a massive volume of traffic and a correspondingly massive sale of tickets. I believe the second of these requirements will be met automatically within a few decades after the first is achieved. There are formidable technical problems involved in producing the reusable orbital vehicle, but I do not believe the problems are permanently insoluble. Few people in the existing space program have worked on these problems, because the policy has been to do things fast rather than cheaply. The present cut-back may in fact encourage more long-range work on cheaper vehicles. I hesitate to make numerical predictions, but it may help to make my remarks meaningful if I state my actual expectations for the time-scale of these developments. I expect that sometime between 50 and 100 years from now we will have space travel with a volume of traffic and a cost to the passen-

gers comparable with our present intercontinental jet
flights. This prediction has the great advantage that if
the reality exceeds my hopes I may be here to enjoy it,
whereas, if I am proved wrong the other way, I will never
know it.

THE BENEFITS

I will not say more about the economic aspects of
space travel. The technical problems can be solved only
by long and hard work, not by philosophical discourse.
I am here discussing the problems of goals and purpose.
Why should so many people want to rush around in
space? And what good will it all do?

First I should like to make clear that I do not envisage
emigration from Earth as solving the problem of the
population explosion. Emigrants will always be a small
minority, like the Spanish conquistadores rather than the
Irish peasants of the Hungry Forties. Those who stay on
Earth must solve their population problems, one way
or another. Those who emigrate will have only postponed
theirs.

I conceive the expansion of mankind into space to
confer benefits on us in three main respects. (I am still
ignoring entirely the scientific benefits and speaking only
of social benefits.) The three benefits I will call garbage
disposal, invulnerability and the open frontier, in what
I consider to be increasing order of importance.

If humanity were to be forever confined to Earth, the
problem of pollution could hardly be solved without an
enforced economic stagnation. Many industrial processes
are inherently messy, and the sum-total of industrial
processes threatens to heat the Earth's biosphere to an
intolerable extent within a century or two at present rates
of economic growth. If cheap space transportation were
available, it would become socially desirable and probably
economically advantageous to move many of the messier
industries into space. The solar wind is a magnificent
garbage-disposal system, sweeping any dispersed matter
in the solar system into the outer darkness where it will
never be seen again. Prime candidates for the move up-

stairs would be the nuclear reactor and processing industries with their very large radioactive waste and thermal pollution problems.

The migration of industry into space need not be directed by a grandiose governmental plan. It would probably occur spontaneously as a result of economic pressures, if polluting industries were forced to pay for the privilege of remaining on Earth the actual cost of their pollutions. I foresee a time, a few centuries from now, when the bulk of heavy industry is space-borne, with the majority of mining operations perhaps transferred to the moon, and the Earth preserved for the enjoyment of its inhabitants as a green and pleasant land.

IF WE ARE LUCKY

If the problem of garbage disposal for an Earth-bound humanity is difficult, the problem of invulnerability is essentially insoluble. How can we expect to go on living forever on this exposed planetary surface, armed with deadly weapons which year by year grow more numerous and more widely dispersed? The only way to make the Earth safe from these weapons would be to establish a supra-national monopoly of military force, and even such a monopoly would not give us permanent security. The guardians of the monopoly would be men with their own national loyalties, and there would always be danger that the monopoly would break up in ruinous civil war, as happened on a smaller scale in 1861. We can hope to survive in a world bristling with hydrogen bombs for a few centuries, if we are lucky. But I believe we have small chance of surviving 10,000 years if we stay stuck to this planet. We are too many eggs in too small a basket.

The emigration into distant parts of the solar system of a substantial number of people would make our species as a whole invulnerable. A nuclear holocaust on Earth would still be an unspeakable tragedy, and might still wipe out 99 per cent of our numbers. But the one per cent who had dispersed themselves could not be wiped out simultaneously by any man-made catastrophe, and they would remain to carry on the promise of our destiny.

Perhaps some of them would also come back to repopu-
late the Earth, after the radioactivity had cooled off. I
at least find it a consoling thought that the human race
will one day be invulnerable, that we have only to survive this awkward period of a century or two between
the discovery of nuclear weapons and the large-scale expansion of our habitat, and then we shall be masters of
our fate, freed from the threat of permanent extinction.

THE OPEN FRONTIER

The third and to my mind deepest benefit which
space offers to mankind is the recovery of an open frontier. At this point we come back to the question: Where
will all these people go when they set out in their latter-
day Mayflowers? It is conventional in science fiction to
think of going to planets, to Mars in particular. But I do
not think planets will play the major role in man's future.
For one thing, they are mostly uninhabitable. For another thing, even if they are habitable they will not
increase our living-space very much. If we succeed in
colonizing Mars, Mars will soon resemble the Earth,
complete with parking lots, income tax forms, and all the
rest of it. It will not be possible to hide on Mars any
more than on Earth.

I believe the real future of man in space lies far away
from planets, in isolated city-states floating in the void,
perhaps attached to an inconspicuous asteroid or perhaps to a comet. Comets are especially important. It is
believed that between a billion and 10 billion comets
exist on the outer fringes of the solar system, loosely attached to the sun and only very rarely passing close to it.
Each of these comets is a mine of biologically useful materials, carbon, nitrogen and water. Together they provide a thousand times as much living space as the planets.
Above all they provide an open frontier, a place to hide
and to disappear without trace, beyond the reach of
snooping policemen and bureaucrats.

This vision of comet-hopping emigrants, streaming
outward like the covered wagons on the Santa Fe Trail,
is perhaps absurdly romantic or fanciful. Maybe it will

never happen the way I imagine it. But I am convinced that something more or less along these lines will ultimately happen. Space is huge enough, so that somewhere in its vastness there will always be a place for rebels and outlaws. Near to the sun, space will belong to big governments and computerized industries. Outside, the open frontier will beckon as it has beckoned before, to persecuted minorities escaping from oppression, to religious fanatics escaping from their neighbors, to recalcitrant teen-agers escaping from their parents, to lovers of solitude escaping from crowds. Perhaps most important of all for man's future, there will be groups of people setting out to find a place where they can be safe from prying eyes, free to experiment undisturbed with the creation of radically new types of human beings, surpassing us in mental capacities as we surpass the apes.

A HOPE FOR MAN

So I foresee that the ultimate benefit of space travel to man will be to make it possible for him once again to live as he lived throughout prehistoric time, in isolated small units. Once again his human qualities of clannish loyalty and exclusiveness will serve a constructive role, instead of being the chief dangers to his survival.

Men's tribal instincts will move back from the destructive channels of nationalism, racism and youthful alienation, and find satisfaction in the dangerous life of a frontier society. Genetic drift and diversification will again become important factors in human progress. Only in this way, I believe, can the basic dilemmas of our age, arising from the discordance between our tribal loyalties and the necessities of a world-wide technological civilization, be resolved. And when the angry young men and rebels and racists have again a frontier to which they can go, perhaps we timid and law-abiding citizens who choose to stay quietly down here on Earth will find it easier to live together in peace.

EUGENE RABINOWITCH

3.   FROM ALAMOGORDO TO APOLLO: WILL MAN HEED THE LESSON?

A landing on the moon and a successful return of American astronauts to Earth must be considered as one of the most exciting moments in human history. In addition to being a great human adventure and an unprecedented deed of exploration, it provides striking revelation of the capacities of contemporary scientific technology. As such, it has great implications for the future. It gives a foretaste of things that can be done— if society has a will to do them.

It was an enormously complex technical operation. Thousands of mechanisms of propulsion, guidance, information and communication had to function without fail, with split-second timing, instantaneously obeying the instructions of computers like genii the orders of Aladdin.

Apollo is the second demonstration of the potentialities of large-scale organized science and technology. The first was the creation of the atom bomb. In four years, backed by an investment of $2 billion, a team of several thousand scientists and engineers forced entrance into the closed world of atomic nuclei, and a new age of human existence—the atomic age—was born.

The moon landing, too, was the product of cooperative efforts of thousands of scientists and technologists. It cost more than 10 times as much as the first atom bomb: the Apollo stage of the program alone has involved the expenditure of $24 billion. However, the annual gross national product of the United States has grown, between

1945 and 1969, from about $250 billion to about $900 billion. To produce the first atom bomb required something like one per cent, and to send the first men to the moon, something like three per cent of our annual GNP.

SPACE AND THE ARMS RACE

The capacity for cosmic exploration arose out of this arms race; the landing on the moon is the outcome of a competition of national technologies for leadership in a deeply-torn world.

Can the dawn of the cosmic age achieve what the dawn of the nuclear age has failed, as yet, to do—inaugurate an era of world-wide cooperation in constructive utilization of the forces of science and technology for common advancement of all men?

There is widespread criticism of the moon-landing program, which even the triumph of Apollo will not squelch. Is the landing on the moon, however spectacular, worth the annual expenditure of $5 billion over several years, while vital social challenges at home and in the world remained unanswered?

On a much greater scale—and with greater justification —a similar question can be asked about the American military budget. Is it justified to spend approximately 70 per cent of the federal budget to keep ahead of the Soviet Union in the number and sophistication of nuclear weapons and delivery rockets—weapons which no American political leader can contemplate using except in desperate retaliation—while not enough money is available for keeping the society, which these arms aim to protect, socially and morally healthy? There seems to be not enough money to end rural poverty and malnutrition, for rescuing cities from apparently inexorable drift toward becoming giant traffic-choked slums, for ending road congestion and road slaughter, for eliminating the ugly and dangerous pollution of air and water, and for stopping the contamination of the soil and of the oceans with persistent chemical and radioactive poisons.

In contrast to the space program, which has spectacularly delivered what it has promised to deliver, the military program is promising what it cannot and will never be able to deliver: security for the American people. The early settlers in the New World had more real security behind a wooden stockade, than we (or the Russians) have behind all the Polarises, Poseidons and Minutemen (or their Soviet equivalents). Both sides will have even less security after they have constructed, at a cost of hundreds of billions of dollars, extensive anti-ballistic missile systems. Military leadership on each side deludes its people and its government (perhaps deludes itself, too) into looking at its latest, and most expensive, program as "the last word," while it merely provokes the other side to pursuing the race another mile. Each side pretends to believe that after it makes the last move, and has a temporary lead in the race, the other side will be more willing to talk about arms control, and both descend deeper and deeper into insecurity.

Quite apart from an end to power politics (which will provide the only stable solution and make disarmament possible) the greatest security by mutual terror could be established for both sides by returning to a limited nuclear deterrent, costing only a fraction of the present military budgets.

COST OF CURING SOCIAL ILLS

Errors of commission—and, even more, those of omission—have led to the accumulation of grave social problems in the wealthiest and most productive nation on Earth. Attempts to estimate the cost of curing these ills indicate that much more is required than could be saved by trimming the military budget of costly programs, such as ABM deployment, not to speak of cutting down the NASA budget, for example, by eliminating manned planetary expeditions.

In the face of a task of this magnitude, a third question cannot be avoided, one rarely heard in American public debate, which concentrates on maldistribution of government spending by excessive attention to weapons and space: Is it proper for Americans to spend two-thirds of their national economic production on satisfaction of their personal needs and desires, which far exceed basic human needs—on more (and fancier) cars, second residences, cosmetics, alcohol, tobacco and travel—while there are not enough funds for the most urgent community programs? Often, this distribution of our national product defeats the very purpose of individual spending.

What is the use of additional millions of private cars if the city streets are so congested that the most luxurious high-speed car cannot move except at a snail's pace; if travel on open roads involves killing and maiming thousands of men, women and children each year, and poisoning the air with exhaust fumes? Should not rehabilitation of cities, and expanding the rapid transit system, take precedence over further multiplication of private cars? Is it reasonable to build more (and more luxurious) private residences outside the blighted cities if the pall from the cities' furnaces and internal combustion engines is permitted to spread unchecked over the surrounding countryside?

WE MUST REVIEW PRIORITIES

What is needed in the face of these challenges is not piecemeal attacks on obvious targets: for some, the ABM deployment or the space program; for others, the relief expenditures or foreign aid. We must have an overall review of national priorities, coupled with imaginative analysis of the possibilities modern technology offers to meet them, and realistic estimates of the costs which effective remedial programs will entail. This unprecedented stock-taking may require political innovation.

Numerous advisory bodies have arisen in recent years, mainly within the executive branch of government, to supply expert advice in various fields, particularly those having important scientific and technological input. In the next decades, advisory bodies oriented to the full spectrum of our social needs may be required to review America's priorities, as well as to evaluate the possibilities which modern science and technology offer in response to the challenges.

In this process of review, neither the space program,

nor the military establishment, nor private spending of
Americans, can remain sacred cows.

At the present time, with a gross national product of
about $900 billion, Americans allow their national gov-
ernment about $160 million, of which close to $100
billion goes to the military establishment, $4 billion to
space projects, and $2 billion to foreign aid. This leaves
about $700 billion to private spending. A re-evaluation of
national priorities may well lead to the conclusion that
our social spending, in order to answer adequately the
most urgent challenges, must be of the order of $300 or
$400 billion a year, including both federal and local ex-
penditures. This may require slashing—perhaps by one-
half—of the military budget, and a substantial cut in
private spending, at least in relation to gross national
income but probably also in absolute amount.

The first aim can be achieved if we give up chasing the
will-of-the-wisp of winning the arms race, and aim instead
merely at retaining the only kind of security which a
nation can have in our time—the precarious security of
the capacity for second strike against any aggressor. The
second aim also can be achieved without undue economic
hardship. This is clearly shown by the experience of
World War II. Public education is needed to make
people aware that to win this peacetime war at home is
no less compelling than was the need to win past wars
abroad.

Within this radically changed order of priorities, continued expenditure of $4 billion for space exploration,
as well as a substantial increase in the foreign aid budget
(now far below the one per cent of gross national income
recommended by the U.N. in the development decade)
will not appear excessive. But if no such fundamental
reassessment of national priorities is made, the drive to
slash the space budget (and practically to kill foreign
aid) in order to free some funds for the most urgent
social programs, may well become irresistible.

If such a general reappraisal is not made, and its conclusions are not implemented after broad public discussion, by democratic procedures, it will be a *testimonium*

paupertatis of democracy, and an invitation to dictatorship.

The rebellion on American campuses has one hopeful aspect: it reveals the discontent of youth with the traditional pursuit of individual advancement, wealth and power; it shows their thirst for public service. The response to the Peace Corps' appeal already has demonstrated the existence of this urge among American youth, who only a few years ago were widely accused of thinking of nothing but personal satisfaction and security.

The task of education in America—from the public school to college—should be to strengthen this dedication to public service, and help devise rational ways to implement this commitment. Skeptics may believe that the American people will not support (except in wartime) national programs requiring substantial sacrifice of personal wishes and ambitions for the common good. We must prove these skeptics to be wrong.

Soviet Academician Andrei Sakharov has drawn, in broad outline, a program for both the United States and the Soviet Union. He envisages America ending its racial troubles in 10 years by self-imposed economic sacrifices of the white majority, and looks for an end to underdevelopment and population pressure everywhere in another 20 years. This he expects to be achieved through allotment of 20 per cent of the gross national product of the advanced countries—the United States, Western Europe, Russia and Japan—to foreign aid: a voluntary belt-tightening by the rich nations to help the poor ones.

Sakharov's time table may be totally unrealistic. But public opinion and political leadership in the West tend to underestimate the capacities of modern science and technology to produce unprecedented changes in human existence, despite the "miracles" of Alamogordo and Cape Kennedy.

WHAT TECHNOLOGY CAN DO

Of course, many—perhaps the most important—social challenges of our time are such that science and technology cannot contribute decisively to answering them.

Racial prejudice and discrimination are among such problems at home. Lack of education, tribal and racial conflicts, persistence of prescientific attitudes and modes of life are obstacles to rapid progress in the underdeveloped parts of the world. But even to these areas, science and technology could make important contributions. It has been said—even if it cannot be proved—that the Vietnam war could have been prevented by early implementation of the Lower Mekong plan, pulling together nations in this whole area, from North Vietnam to Thailand, in common economic development. It is possible that the Middle East war could have been warded off by large-scale investment in desalination of sea water. Alvin Weinberg of Oak Ridge has emphasized the capacity of such "technlogical fixes" to by-pass apparently insoluble social deadlocks. They may be unjustifiable by traditional economic criteria, but compared to the human and economic costs of a Vietnam war, or a repeated Arab-Israeli confrontation, these criteria must be rejected as irrelevant.

Many other social problems of our time are much more strongly technological, and clearly call for technological solutions: pollution, traffic congestion, even the decay of cities.

In space programs and, even more, in weapons development, false starts and the waste of millions, if not billions, of dollars have been and always will remain inevitable. (Cancellation of the Manned Orbiting Laboratory (MOL) announced this June by the Pentagon, after the expenditure of nearly $1.3 billion, is the latest example.) Such failures are accepted, by Congress and the public, as penalties for venturing into new, unexplored areas. In asking for funding of the Safeguard project, the Pentagon is not restrained by the fiasco of the Nike-Zeus project a few years ago.

An even greater risk of false starts and large losses will be inevitable in large-scale attempts to solve social problems by technological means. "Social engineering" is as unexplored a field now as nuclear engineering was in 1940 or space engineering in 1960. Each failure in this area is bound to lead to accusations of incompetence and boondoggling; but we should be prepared to bear with them and learn from mistakes to do better in the next attempt.

These are some thoughts provoked by the great enterprise of Apollo. If it will impress American society with the capacity of science and technology, properly supported, to do things which may have seemed impossible a few years ago, if it will contribute to reexamination of our national priorities and to a search for those among them where imaginative use of science and technology could contribute to success, the moon landing may prove to be worth its costs—quite independently of its direct contributions to physical sciences and space exploration, and a most thrilling human adventure.

PART II

THE POLITICS OF SPACEFARING

SIDNEY HYMAN

4. MAN ON THE MOON:
THE COLUMBIAN DILEMMA

On Friday morning, October 12, 1492, Christopher
Columbus, Admiral of the Ocean, debarked from the
Santa Maria, a decked ship of 100 tons. Joining him on
shore when he unfurled the royal standard of Spain were
the captains of the *Pinta* and *Nina*, each a caravel of 50
tons, and most the 88 men comprising the different
crews. All now "kissed the ground with tears of joy" and
"gave thanks to God for the great mercy received." Then
the Admiral named the place San Salvador and solemnly
took possession of it on behalf of his royal patrons, Ferdinand and Isabella of Castile and Leon. Then, too, such
of the crews as had been mutinous on the 70-day voyage
from Spain prostrated themselves at the feet of Columbus and weepingly sought his pardon.

Five months later, in mid-March, 1493, Columbus was
in Barcelona where he was received in full court by Ferdinand and Isabella and heaped with honors. True, he had
yet to prove his theory that because of the spheric shape
of the Earth a ship sailing west from Europe into the
setting sun could reach Asia. Nor could he claim to have
discovered a continental land mass. His new found lands
so far consisted only of five islands. Yet the Spanish court
which heard Columbus speak and also saw the "rich and
strange spoils" he had brought back from his wanderings
—gold, cotton, curious arms, mysterious flora and fauna,
Indians to be baptized—readily agreed that "something
else" must follow from the extraordinary event.

They were in error on this side of understatement.

BEYOND OUR GRASP

Could any man then alive foresee how the discovery
of the New World would profoundly change virtually all
existing relationships in Europe—that virtually nothing
would ever again be the same, not in politics, economics,
technology, culture, religion, diplomacy, military defense? Could they foresee what would happen because
of the tremendous new idea that "out there," beyond the
western horizon, was a place to which men could escape
and start life anew as if on the first day of a Second
Creation? The most prophetic of men in mid-March
1493 could not even begin to imagine these things. It
was only in a long retrospect, after many generations had
passed by, that the full consequences of the Columbian
discovery became visible—including the "poetic" fact
that it was the American children of the New World
discovered by Columbus who would first succeed in putting a man on the moon.

Right now the honest thing to say is that we are in a
position symmetrical with the one prevailing in Barcelona in mid-March 1493. We can no more grasp the full
political implications of the moon landing than the court
of Ferdinand and Isabella could foresee the great chain
of things forming the sequel to what Columbus had discovered.

At every stage in the evolution of manned space flight,
there were moments when only a man with the soul of a
slave did not stand in awe before what had been achieved.
The target was known. Yet the idea that human bodies
—in collaboration with a reliable technology they had
produced—would at last touch a celestial object at which
mankind had gazed and wondered since the time of Gen-
esis, stood on a plane of its own.

Our instincts alone tell us that the achievement will
rank as more than a self-contained technological work of
art, complete in itself like a finished painting. Here is
something like the quantum jump which took place
when the first organism that was to evolve into man,
crawled out of the sea of primordial slime to start a cycle

of development on solid land. Our instincts alone tell us that the same Promethean ambition which sent man to the moon—an almost compulsive genetic ambition to master and possess nature (in fulfillment of a Biblical promise)—augmented with the return to Earth of the lunar astronauts. It will lead on to other things that will far outstrip the immediate political purposes President John F. Kennedy had in mind when, in the infant days of the space age, he proposed and then launched what became the Apollo program.

But what other things?

Only the passing years can answer the question by revealing what the days now hide about the full political consequences of the moon landing. Science, to be sure, reasons from the known to the unknown. But when we move from the sphere of science to the sphere of politics, can we confidently say—as some people do—that what we now know about the sequel to the Columbian discovery of the New World also forecasts the sequels to man's arrival on the moon? There is indeed something to be gained in understanding by holding the two events in a single vision. Perhaps the greater part of the gain is a warning not to face the future with plans based on nothing more than false analogies spun out of tenuous similarities.

APOLLO AND COLUMBUS

The main resemblances between the Columbian discoveries and the moon-landing appear in their origins. Both were concerned with transportation. Both were preceded by disputes about their feasibility, and a different "order of priorities." Both at their inception were "state financed." Both were born in the context of a Cold War between the West and the East—between Christians and Moslems in the case of the Columbian project, between the "free world" and the Soviet controlled Communist bloc in the case of the Apollo project. Also in the immediate background of both ventures was a distinctive expansion of the human mind—the Renaissance in the first case, and the post-World War II explosion in science and technology in the second. At their inception, the scientific underpinning for both projects combined a mixture of observed fact, conjectures, free wheeling assumptions, legends—many of which later underwent correction. In both cases also, the purely scientific aspects of the project could not by themselves have commanded "state support" on any significant scale if it were not for the fact that both were tied at the hip-bone to political-economic-military aims.

These aims, where the Columbian project was concerned, could be expressed in a straightforward proposition. If a westerly all-water trade route to Asia was found, then European commerce with the Orient would no longer be at the mercy of the Turks, who because of their military hold on Constantinople, could block the movement of that trade over the old routes through the Middle East.

POLITICAL RATIONALE

As for the Apollo project, its political-economic-military aims were derived in good measure from an intersection among four lines of force. One was the successful manned orbital flights of the Soviet cosmonauts, Gagarin and Titov. Next, and immediately after this successful Soviet manned space flight, Nikita Khrushchev gave voice to a spread eagle threat: The USSR, said he, could replace its cosmonauts with megaton nuclear bombs that could be directed to any place on earth. Third, while the Soviet success shook the foundations of American prestige around the world, those foundations were shaken from another side by the bumbling management in the White House which led to the Bay of Pigs fiasco. Fourth, and on top of everything else, though President Kennedy in the 1960 election contest had promised "to get America moving again," the nation's economy in the early 1960s remained sluggish, and the Congress showed little inclination to revive it by approving various domestic measures then under discussion.

These four things together, as seen by President Kennedy and his advisers, combined to make the political-economic-military rationale for the Apollo program. A world grown suddenly skeptical about America's talent for organizing and successfully executing physical projects of great complexity must learn anew that America's technical efficiency and the products of its industry were unmatched in excellence. Hence if America put a man on the moon within an announced set period, the event would be viewed by the world as a trade mark certifying the supremacy of America's management skill and technical power. At the same time, from a purely domestic standpoint, a Congress that had balked at stimulating the economy by other means under discussion, would stimulate it through the funds the Congress was ready to appropriate for the "space program"—especially ready because the program had "national defense" overtones.

Offsetting the resemblances, however, the Columbian discoveries and the Apollo program differ profoundly in many fundamental ways. Merely to touch on a few of these is to see the need for caution before leaping to the conclusion that we can find in the sequel to Columbus' venture the sequel that will now follow the moon landing.

First, there are the profound differences in the technology of the two undertakings. The Columbian enterprise did not call for specially designed tools. There was no need to create new industries in order to produce the tools. It did not require a crew of picked men specially trained in the use of the tools. The tools were in common use among mariners, and had evolved over several thousand years. When funds were in hand, they could be readily acquired from existing sources of supply. As for the crews, the training required was so small, that in the search for sailors, indemnities were offered to criminals and to other "broken" men if they agreed to serve on the expedition.

Furthermore, apart from the usual ship supplies stored for the ocean voyage, it was not necessary for the men on the expedition to envelop themselves in an artificial environment. The sea over which they sailed lay beneath the same ocean of air whose total weight exerted the same pressure of 14.7 pounds per square inch on the Earth's surface at sea level. Once the expedition was on its way, it was on its own. Its motions, survival and return did not depend on the concerted work of technicians who controlled its course at a distance. Finally, when resources were found at the discovery end which were commercially valuable and promised returns far greater than the costs of getting at them, what began as a state venture in exploitation of the New World was transformed in the course of time into private ventures which were within the means of private individuals or groups.

THE NEW VOYAGING

The direct opposite has been true of the man-in-space program. It is true that the program was preceded by a long intellectual history in which each conceptual phase set the stage for the next one. It is also true that its technological preconditions were attained in successive steps. Yet everything that went before evolved without conscious plan until a moment in time was reached where a specific decision was made and whose execution went forward under a wholly new system of rational plans and elaborate controls. New things had to be created for all aspects of the program—new tools, new industries, new environments, new men to produce the tools and environments, new men to use the tools in the new environment, new men newly grouped around the world to direct the movements of the whole business.

Here, by itself, in the mere act of organizing and executing the man-in-space program was a wholly new world, created by government, managed from within by a new elite brotherhood of scientists and technicians with their own special focus of interest, their own heroes, their own urge to maintain themselves as an elitist brotherhood.

The very existence of this new world of collective mental effort—of a special society within a society—may have as great a political impact on the shape of the future as any other kind of "fallout" from the space program. It is still too early to tell the exact form this political impact will take. It is, nonetheless, fair to call attention to the prospect itself—considering how often in ages past, a newly emergent elite in command of a new technology displaced and declassed an existing elite allied to an old technology, and then proceeded from a position of supremacy to imprint its own order of values on people in the mass.

NEW WORLD OF SPACE

As things stand, no private individual or group of private individuals could conjure up and organize the division of scientific and technological labor at the heart of the new world of space. Private enterprise has entered the field of communication satellites in collaboration with many governments. But as things now stand, no private individual could embark on an interplanetary voyage unless he were aided by the whole of the state-run space apparatus. At current estimated cost of $15,000 a pound to get anything into space, the transportation charge to a celestial body—just to touch it, or to start life anew on it, or to collect raw material on it for use on Earth is, therefore, beyond the reach of even the most affluent individuals.

On the same grounds, short of a tremendous breakthrough in cost reduction, one must stamp a large question mark on the illusion that the Earth's population pressures can be eased by rocket immigrations on celestial Mayflowers which will colonize the moon, Mars, Venus, or points beyond. The world population is indeed increasing at an alarming rate. United Nations demographers estimate at least six billion earthlings by the year A.D. 2000. It is thus natural for imaginative and deeply concerned men to invoke other planets of the solar system as the New World was invoked to redress population problems of the Old World.

NO PLACE FOR MAN

Yet the total emigration from the Old World to the New in a century and a half at the peak of immigration was only 50 million—a rate which falls far short of even approaching the annual increases in population nowadays. In this view of the matter alone, migration to other planets does not seem a very realistic solution to population pressures on earth.

For pedagogical purposes alone, it is worthwhile to ask a hypothetical question based on arbitrary assumptions. Suppose that tomorrow, 50 million people were lined up for immigration to another planet. Suppose (contrary to the probabilities in a real situation) that there were no economies of scale. Suppose that the present costs of $15,000 to put a pound of material into space remained constant. Suppose that the 50 million people who had been lined up weighed on the average 130 pounds each. How much would it cost to lift these people into space? The skywriting sum amounts to ninety-seven trillion, five hundred billion dollars—or almost 122 times the current gross national product of the United States. And this figure leaves out of account all other factors such as the habitability of other planets and their capacity to sustain life free of any dependence on artificial environments. None that we know in the solar system is habitable by man.

It may be more realistic to think in terms of routine terrestrial flights by rocket spacecraft, as a logical extension of supersonic and hypersonic transportation in the aerospace medium. Persons with respectable credentials who are associated with the Douglas Aircraft Company's Advance Launch Vehicle Section have described a potentially feasible spacecraft capable of delivering 170 passengers and eighteen tons of cargo to any point on earth within forty-five minutes, at average speeds of 17,000 miles per hour, without subjecting the passengers to any more than three gravities during boost or atmospheric entry. The design is such that its authors believe the spacecraft conceivably could be operational in the early 1980s.

CRITICAL MASSES

An operational spacecraft, of course, does not necessarily mean a commercially feasible spacecraft. But in the instant case, if the economics of the matter are favorable, then the political consequences can be very great indeed. Consequences of this kind always follow anything which contracts time-space relationships, and which facilitates the swift movement of men, material, methods and ideas over great distances. This is not the same as saying that the mere act of bringing people "closer together" is always a political good. If a lifeless comb drawn through human hair crackles with electricity, it is not surprising that the closer masses of people get, and the more they rub together, the more they may feel entrapped, outraged, irritated with each other, and the more they may feel inclined to trample down the atmosphere itself in an explosion of demonic mass violence, as if in a war of all against all.

But leaving this apocalyptic vision out of account, and leaving out of account all the economic and political dislocations that may follow the obsolescence of old means of transport in favor of commercially feasible terrestrial flights by rocket spacecraft, we may be confronted with the political need to look again at the federal government's power to regulate commerce. To put the matter directly: By the rule of analogy, can existing domestic regulations be extended to cover the registration, certification and maintenance of spacecraft for terrestrial flights—along with the certification of spacemen, the regulation of the use of space, and traffic control in space? Can it be extended with the aid of some amendments? Or will the creation of "public order" in connection with these spacecraft flights call for something wholly new in general principles and specific details. In the years ahead, the legal order which is closely tied to the political order may have to ask and answer another kind of question. Does the concept of the "reasonable man" as it relates to behavior on Earth, stand up under conditions of space flight or life on a celestial planet? Or if such conditions materially alter human perceptions and reactions, will jurists have to evolve a new concept of the "reasonable man" in dealing with cases involving episodes in space? Or how can a judge and jury know what is "reasonable" in space if they have not had per-

sonal experiences in space which would provide them
with a fund of "conventional wisdom"? Beyond such
questions, the mind boggles when it thinks about what
a "Presidential election" would be like if it involved a
constituency on one or another celestial planet.

What has been said so far was centered on the profound differences between the Columbian discoveries
and the factors involved in the moon-landing. One more
difference on this head is worth adding here.

Soon after Columbus returned to Spain from his first
voyage into the New World, Pope Alexander VI issued
bulls confirming to the Crowns of Castile and Leon all
the lands discovered, or to be discovered west of a line of
demarcation drawn 100 leagues west of the Azores on
the same terms as those in which the Portuguese held
their colonies along the African coast. Discovery in this
case meant sovereign national possession, and sovereign
national possession in turn meant the freedom of the
sovereign to act as it pleased within the boundaries
possessed.

SOVEREIGNTY IN SPACE

In the space age, by contrast, there is no papal bull
which draws lines of sovereignty on the moon or any
other celestial body. There is instead a treaty on space
signed in Washington, Moscow and London on January
27, 1967, by sixty states. Its avowed object is to reduce
the danger of a conflict among nations in space, and also
to reduce the danger that things done in space will have
disastrous consequences for the Earth and all who dwell
on it.

Thus, among other things, the treaty expressly de-
clares that the moon and other celestial bodies are not
subject to national appropriation by claim of sovereignty,
use, occupation or by any other device. This does not
mean, however, that a nation cannot take effective possession of portions of a celestial land mass such as the
moon. It simply means that it cannot claim the sovereign
right of ownership over the land mass it effectively pos-
sesses. As the line in the song goes, "the moon belongs

to everyone"—even though the best things in life are hardly free.

The treaty, furthermore, prohibits the stationing in outer space of an installation or object carrying a nuclear weapon or any other weapon of mass destruction. It also prohibits the establishment on celestial bodies of military bases and fortifications, the testing of weapons or the conduct of military maneuvers on those celestial bodies. It does, however, permit the use of military personnel for scientific research or for any other peaceful purposes, as well as the use of any equipment or facilities needed for the peaceful exploration of celestial bodies.

In another of its features, the treaty says that the nation which lists on its registry certain objects and personnel that are in outer space or on a celestial body, retains jurisdiction and control over them. But this is coupled with realities falling outside the frame of the treaty. One reality is that the military services of a state have jurisdiction over such personnel as are in the armed forces wherever they may be. Another is that the U.S. Air Defense Command, or its equivalent in the case of the Soviet Union and perhaps other countries, monitors both air space and outer space. It has the job of riding herd on every man-made object in orbit around the Earth, to keep the growing traffic under surveillance, to detect signs of hostile intent and to destroy such hostile objects. If so, then an old condition of peril we have had to live with on Earth, reappears in outer space as well. Once again, we live by the slender margin of the self-discipline, rationality and political sensibilities animating our professional specialists in violence. For the possibility exists that the military services, through their jurisdiction over their own personnel wherever they may be, can trigger clashes in outer space which may spread a contagion of havoc over the face of the Earth.

ENVOYS OF MAN

There is, of course, a provision of the space treaty which exhorts states to cooperate with each other and to render mutual assistance in their explorations and the use of outer space. Astronauts are expressly defined as "envoys of mankind." When they are on celestial bodies, they are enjoined to render all possible assistance to one another. Similarly, a nation on whose territory the astronaut of another nation has been forced to land because of an accident or emergency, is enjoined to give him all possible assistance, including safe return. States are also exhorted to avoid harmful contamination both of celestial bodies and of the environment of the Earth in their space activities. If potential harmful interference with activities of another treaty state is foreseen, appropriate international consultations are to be undertaken upon the request of any of the states concerned before proceeding with the activity planned.

These exhortations to mutual helpfulness among nations participating in space activities are not to be scoffed at. They are in the spirit of an ancient phrase conveying an insight that is often overlooked: "His own light shines no less when he hath lit another's lamp therefrom." Still, unless man behaves in the heavens in a far nobler way than he behaves on Earth, the spirit of mutual helpfulness and cooperation which infuses the space treaty may last only so long as the resources of the planets remain unknown or only touched in a fugitive way. But suppose priceless resources were in fact found in outer space? Suppose the means were found to exploit them either by colonies established on the planets, or by their shipment back to Earth? What then?

As things currently stand, there is nothing to encourage the belief that the old story of grabbing and getting will not start all over again in outer space.

Ordinarily, it is a reasonable procedure to allow the laws for public order in space to develop with emergent real needs, as against the alternative of having the law precede the specific shape the needs take. Yet the case ahead in space is not ordinary. There is nothing to be lost and perhaps something to be gained if steps are taken right now to study and report on the possibilities of international accords on points of detail which are not covered by the space treaty. Among other things, there is the need to explore the possibilities of reaching international accords on the utilization of land masses in space, the definition of rights of accession to mineral or other resources, the benefits and obligations of settlements, the resolution of disputes, the order of civil and criminal laws, and the system of governmental administration. If nothing else, the exercise might have the virtue of bringing home to the ideologues of America and the Soviet Union that their economic and political systems are not divine expressions of what God made for man, but are expressions of what man made for himself whether out of his wisdom or his folly.

There is room for a final comment.

In judging political trends, it is always hard to distinguish between transient moods and deep running currents. So, too, if we ask whether the American people will lend their political support to a continued and perhaps expanded space program, we face a difficult task in first trying to distinguish between what is transient and what is deep rooted in the manifestations of political resistance the program has encountered.

We know that successive phases of the space program to date coincided with a widening breach in the American community due to the bitter controversy over the conduct of the Vietnamese war, and to the outburst of rebellions in the cities and the universities. In this context, a chorus of sober voices was heard to say on all sides that the moon-landing program was the supreme emblem of America's wrong priorities—that it made no sense to appropriate billions of dollars to put a man on the moon while denying even a small portion of those billions to programs that could put millions of submerged Americans back on their feet on the American earth. No achievement in space, say these voices, has in any way bettered conditions on Earth. It only makes it possible for "wickedness to go faster" at great expense, while conditions at home grow ever worse from neglect.

A NEW AGE

Is the argument to this effect the product of a profound "disillusion with progress"? Or is it the product of a specific set of circumstances—all related to the malignancy of the Vietnamese conflict—and subject to change if and when that conflict is ended as it someday must be? I could be in gross error, but I would judge that the latter instead of the former probability is closer to the truth. I would judge that once the malignancy of the Vietnamese conflict is removed, the perceptions of Americans will be opened more fully to the changes in outlook, born in the space age, that are even now fermenting quietly in the recesses of our minds.

The urgency of a program to deal with poverty in the ghettoes speaks for itself. It is visible, tactile. But one wonders whether, in the long run, the whole politics of a society is not more profoundly changed by a new insight into the infinite capabilities of man and a change in his perceptions about time, space and land than can be inferred from statutes addressed to an immediate problem. If the answer is "Yes," then it is conceivable that the space program, without conscious intent, may even now be ushering in a new political age.

CHARLES S. SHELDON II

5. AN AMERICAN "SPUTNIK" FOR THE RUSSIANS?

The Soviet Union for some years has been describing itself as the world leader in space, and making quite explicit that this leadership is the hallmark of an overall pattern of progress related to the superiority of its social and political system. The American Apollo landing the first men on the moon might raise questions about the Soviet claims. The purpose of this article is to explore the feelings and the effects on policy which may follow from so historic an American "first" in space.

THE 1955–1961 ERA

It is hard to realize the United States and the Soviet Union announced their respective plans to launch scientific satellites as part of the International Geophysical Year (IGY) only 14 years ago in July 1955. Much has happened since to transform our technology and our world position.

In the following two years, the public was treated to cut-away drawings of a 20-pound Vanguard; as intermediate test flights occurred, they were received with polite interest and probably a feeling of confidence that the United States would once again demonstrate preeminence in applied technology by launching the first satellite.

Despite a few warning voices and usually ignored Soviet announcements which grew more explicit with time, the successful launching of Sputnik on October 4, 1957, caught both the public and the technical community by surprise. All over the world people went out to search the night skies for the winking traverse of light from the tumbling spent rocket-casing of the Soviet flight. The payload was 184 pounds, and the rocket in orbit was probably about six tons and as long as a Pullman car.

In the weeks which followed, detractors in the Western world began to explain away the Soviet surprise. A "hunk of cast iron," a "basket ball in space," a "silly bauble" was unimportant and unimpressive. The whole thing "had been done with mirrors" and "false radio signals." The Russians had spent an "inordinate amount of money," had "failed many times," had "missed celebrating the birthday of Tsiolkovsky on September 17."

But there were other accounts in the popular press which implied that an immediate strategic military shift in the balance of power had occurred, permitting our potential enemy to drop nuclear weapons from orbit without warning. These latter accounts took little measure of the realities of celestial mechanics, the energy requirements, the problems of command and control and of reliability, or of the war-game hypotheses to be tested for various potential deployments of space weapons.

More sober assessments of the significance of the Soviet triumph both compromised the extreme views, and opened up new avenues for consideration. The United States was profoundly affected by Sputnik, and perhaps not in ways the Soviet Union had fully anticipated. Not that this would necessarily have changed their plans. The Senate Preparedness Subcommittee, in the late fall of 1957, conducted extensive hearings on missiles and space. In the winter of 1958, both houses of Congress established ad hoc committees, chaired by their respective majority leaders, to consider legislative needs to meet the new problems of the dawning space age. Added urgency had come from the ignominious first launch of the widely publicized Vanguard which exploded into a ball of fire on the launch pad in December 1957. The United States Congress speedily moved to meet the science crisis as the legislators saw it. Through the spring of 1958, they considered a complex piece of legislation, and, by summer, the National Aeronautics and Space Act was signed into law with an infusion of new funds for space work.

The reaction was far wider than establishing a post-IGY space program. For the first time, the President appointed a full-time Science Advisor. Attention was given to long-term manpower problems in science and engineering. There was concern about the support of both basic and applied research. A sharp upward shift occurred in research and development expenditures in virtually all fields, with especial emphasis in defense as well as space. The quality of science education came under searching review, and there was enthusiasm for building courses in new math, chemistry, biology, and physics. Scholarships and fellowships became more plentiful in the hard sciences.

While percentage shifts in expenditures were most marked immediately following Sputnik, selective increases, particularly in space, were even greater in absolute terms when the Soviet Union, in 1961, underscored its serious commitment to space flight by sending Gagarin around the Earth. The reaction of the United States was to give almost unanimous congressional support to President Kennedy for the Apollo lunar landing project.

THE SOVIET LONG-TERM COMMITMENT TO SPACE

We can only surmise the full extent of Soviet planning for space. They do not reveal budget data, their organizational patterns, or even the names of their space leaders. Long after the fact, we learned they had created as early as 1953, five years ahead of the National Aeronautics and Space Administration (NASA), a permanent commission on interplanetary travel within the Soviet Academy of Sciences. While the United States planned a 20-pound Vanguard around non-military rocketry, the Soviet Union committed their original ICBM to parallel space duties. Designed before the thermonuclear breakthrough to lightweight warheads, this monster rocket with a first stage thrust of over one million pounds continues to be the standard launch vehicle, even though it has been superseded by newer, more effective ICBMs for military purposes. Used very inefficiently for the first Sputnik launch, this rocket now, with more nearly optimized upper staging, places up to 16,500 pounds in orbit, and is used even for the Soyuz generation of manned craft.

The generally orderly unfolding of the Soviet pattern of space flights suggests that they may be operating with a long-range plan covering a span of 20 to 25 years, even though actual events require changing specific timetables. Conversations with Russian scientists suggest that even they were a little surprised by the speed with which manned flights were accomplished. Whatever the facts, it is evident from a review of the Soviet literature and news releases that the Soviet Union has talked quite consistently from 1957 of opening the entire solar system in the years ahead to Soviet manned flight, and, as practical, to Soviet colonization of the planets. Such statements of prediction or philosophy have been weak on precise timetables, but strong in conviction, and have come from engineers, high science officials, military generals and the top party leadership.

One can credit the Soviet Union with a fairly quick realization of a space program's potential for supporting multiple national objectives. They saw opportunities to advance science, as evidenced by their commitment of as much as 20 per cent of their total launch attempts to lunar and planetary flight compared with about 6 per cent in the United States. They saw a tie between strategic military operations and space, and have left actual flight operations in the hands of their military rocket forces. They have also displayed considerable skill in emphasizing the political significance of space flight as a means of rallying national pride and fervor and of impressing on the uncommitted world the likelihood of Soviet leadership and success in its undertakings in many fields. It has been argued that the early Sputniks were more than paid for by the post-Sputnik rises in exports of Soviet machinery and technical goods due to the increased confidence of foreign buyers.

Strangely, despite this vision of the potential of space and awareness of practical applications, as shown in the Soviets' literature, they were quite slow to apply space hardware to weather reporting, communications, and military support flights, as compared with the United States. While the United States began such work in the 1950s, the first Soviet flights of these types did not appear until the Kosmos program began in 1962, and, in several instances, Soviet results were so marginal that such applications were not even acknowledged until 1965. By that time, the United States had moved on to later generation craft with greater refinements and longer operational life.

SOVIET INTEREST IN THE MOON

While Soviet flights into deep space could be judged as having basic science objectives, the flights to the moon in particular could also be viewed as chiefly for the purpose of gathering engineering data required for later manned landings. Thus the 27 pictures of the surface taken by Luna 9 and the soil impact tests of Luna 13 answered the specific question of whether or not a manned craft could land in comparison with the broader objectives of 100,000 U.S. Surveyor lunar surface views. Gravity anomalies important to flight control were studied by Luna 10-12 and 14, while detailed reconnaissance of landing sites could be obtained from the United States efforts.

Virtually up until the time of Apollo 8, Soviet cosmonauts on foreign goodwill tours were permitted to say that when the Americans reach the moon, "we will be there to greet them." Indeed, it was widely assumed that the Soviet Union would conduct a manned circumlunar flight just before the 50th anniversary of the October Revolution in 1967. The press gave several indications of possible preparations. Two test flights were judged by the British to be the heaviest to reach orbit. An elaborate tracking ship, the "Kosmonaut Vladimir Komarov," was

located in the tropical waters of the western Atlantic to
fill in a gap in the Soviet deep space network. If such a
flight was planned, technical problems interfered, and
the anniversary instead stressed the successes of the
Kosmos 186-188 docking and the Venera 4 penetration
of Venus's atmosphere.

During 1968, the Proton class launch vehicle with a
first stage thrust of over three million pounds was used
to send unmanned Zond payloads around the moon followed by recovery on Earth. These were later identified
by the Russians as precursors to manned flights. But
Proton is not powerful enough by itself to launch a
manned landing and return expedition.

One proposed Soviet solution is the establishment in
Earth orbit of an orbital launch facility, a major assembly and fueling station where a lunar craft could be prepared. The several Soviet space dockings point this way,
but represent a rudimentary beginning, considering eight
to ten Proton payloads would be required for the lunar
ship and its fuel, and such a virtuoso performance was
very unlikely before the scheduled launch of Apollo.

An alternative would be the use of a Saturn V class or
larger Soviet launch vehicle for a direct flight. High
NASA officials have testified before Congress to their
belief that such a vehicle is approaching flight readiness.
Because of Soviet knowledge of the Apollo timetable,
and the time their conservative practices should allow
for man-rating a new Soviet vehicle, they may be suffering program slippage here as well as in circumlunar
flight.

Some Americans assume the opposite view, that the
United States has been tricked into a non-existent race,
while the Soviet Union will concentrate on Earth orbital
applications and deep space unmanned scientific flights.
This view could no more be proved to everyone's satisfaction than the supposition of a Soviet attempt to be
first to land men. A test flight of a very large vehicle
would have supported the contest assumption.

There is an outside chance, though remote, that the
Russians on a first flight of a new large vehicle would

put in Earth orbit an unmanned lunar landing assemblage employing the tested Proton for its upper stages; then a human crew in the Soyuz class ship would rendezvous and transfer into the moon ship.

SOVIET PROBLEMS IN THEIR SPACE PROGRAM

Some of the Soviet problems have been identified in the foregoing discussion, but not the root causes. For all their long-range planning in the mid-1950s, it seems likely that the Russians were caught by surprise, both by the world impact of their successes and the speed with which the implications for a comprehensive program were translated into a need for a larger investment in facilities and hardware. Between 1957 and 1962, they relied exclusively on the one standard vehicle and presumably a few launch pads at Tyuratam. In 1962, they had to open new facilities at Kapustin Yar for a more modest vehicle to round out other parts of a total program, and by 1966, Plesetsk was also brought into use to conduct recurrent operational programs so that Tyuratam could be used to concentrate on research and development and on more specialized manned and deep space missions. It took some years for production rates of vehicles to rise to the present high level which is in excess of that of the United States.

The Russians used to imply they had no space failures, but because they are building on the same technology base that we are, and our failure rate overall has been about 19 per cent, we can be sure they have troubles too. This has been particularly evident in Soviet launches timed to match known deep space "windows" which have resulted in tumbling debris in Earth orbit.

COMPARATIVE BENEFITS

One gains the impression that the Soviet Union moves more rapidly to all-up testing of space projects in actual flight with less ground testing than is common to U.S. practice. Our extensive testing explains some of our high program costs but generally good results, and our often duplicated facilities at NASA, Defense, and industry

sites give us a strong base for expanded work should the
need arise. Soviet skimping may save money and time,
but seems to have had a price, especially in upper stage
and payload failures.

Soviet electronic failures have also been prevalent.
The Soviet Union met early needs with off-the-shelf
items sealed in pressurized compartments equivalent to
Earth surface atmospheres because they were not weight-
limited in launch vehicles. Now they must work to catch
up with the U.S. state of the art, whereas we were forced
to design earlier for the rigorous demands of space.

For a long time, Soviet claims of leadership in space
were indisputable because they were backed by evidence.
But gradually the picture changed so that a case could
be made by partisans in either country that one or the
other country was ahead. There were so many competi-
tions, it was not surprising "firsts" sometimes fell to one
country and sometimes to the other.

Leadership in manned flight definitely rested with the
Russians during the Vostok and Mercury period, and
seemed to when Voskhod carried the first three-man
crew and then provided the first extra-vehicular activity
(EVA). Yet, strangely, Soviet manned activity ceased
for more than two years, while Gemini picked up broad
new experience in maneuver, rendezvous, docking, external powered assist to an altitude of 851 miles, stay times
up to 14 days (the Soviet record, five days) and 12 hours
of EVA (the Soviet total, then 10 minutes). Soviet pub-
licists praised the bravery of our men, scorned the waste-
fulness of repetitive flights, and promised greater Soviet
triumphs in the future.

By early 1967, U.S. confidence was at a high level,
when suddenly the disastrous fire on the pad at Cape
Kennedy killed the first Apollo crew. The Russian reaction was sympathetic, but implied they took fewer risks
because of an absence of corporate greed. Three months
later, the first flight of the advanced Soyuz craft was
advertised as about to be the most exciting manned
flight to date. Instead, Colonel Komarov was called down
after one day of routine checks, and in the final stage of

re-entry, twisted parachute lines permitted the ship to plunge to Earth at high speed, killing him. Now both countries had lost men in connection with their space-craft. Both countries found the experiences sobering, and had delays of a year and a half before they could resume flights with improved vehicles.

The flight of Apollo 8 with 10 orbits of the moon brought generous Soviet praise, but its coverage was somewhat overshadowed by publicity on a year-long ground test of a Soviet sealed space cabin. The Apollo 8 success was so undeniable that little could be done to offset it, aside from references to the high risks.

As American preparations advanced toward the lunar landing, the Soviet talk of being first in all major achievements largely ceased. Boris Petrov, on April 24, 1969, denied a Soviet race for the lunar landing, stressed Soviet concern with safety and with purely scientific objectives.

EFFECTS ON SOVIET SOCIETY OF THE APOLLO LANDING SUCCESS

However the news is handled, one can surmise that thoughtful Soviet citizens may question as an article of faith the inevitable triumph of Soviet technology. Such feelings may find most outspoken expression in the semi-underground anti-establishment movements of Soviet society. This is not to say their poets and novelists will approve of U.S. space flight objectives or national policies. They do not like our military actions and our domestic racial problems. Yet some Soviet youth may ape even more Western clothing styles and music. Individual Russians may speak more openly for greater cooperation, not only in space flight but on other technological problems.

The Soviet government is partly responsive to public attitudes, but typically still plans from the top down. Hence we must consider not only the propaganda and opinion consequences of the Apollo triumph, but the possible effects in Soviet ruling circles of party, the ministries, and the military.

It seems likely the Soviet leadership, no matter how

cynical in certain matters, really believes science can be applied to advancing the Soviet system. Space, as a selected area for application of advanced technology, is looked upon not just for propaganda successes, but as a tool for mastering man's environment, and for spreading his accomplishments throughout the solar system. Space work will not pave the local roads to collective farms, or repair the falling plaster and disabled elevators in Soviet housing projects. But whatever the problems of technology transfer, there is a real change in the nature of modern technological society in both the Soviet Union and the United States as a result of the heavy commitment to space development.

Undoubtedly, certain fields are experiencing the change first: segments of the machine industry, armaments, electronics, optics, and instrumentation. Beyond this, there are new concepts of quality control, better products in metallurgy, plastics, ceramics, fiber composites, and so forth. Soviet processes and products are showing a marked improvement in precision and in application of automatic machines. Although the Soviet Union is believed to lag behind the United States in its electronics and its trend toward integrated circuits, the gap which may be two to four years is not very significant in light of the rush toward improvements in these areas. Some Soviet hardware in applications such as radar, communications, and instrumentation may be equal or superior to competitive products anywhere. Soviet systems applications developed for space are available for a far wider range of industrial, transportation, resource extraction, military, and social problems. A nation capable of mounting a large space program can take on a wide range of difficult but possible tasks that no earlier generation would have had the temerity to consider.

FUTURE SOVIET DIRECTION

Now what will be the impact of the American lunar landing success on Soviet society? How will the Soviet authorities respond? To a degree the special mystique of

Soviet scientific and technical superiority in space will be punctured badly, if not shattered. The evidence of the American triumph will be so overwhelming that propagandists could hardly pass it off as just risk-taking and luck. Such logic pushed too far in light of the obvious careful and comprehensive preparations in the United States will raise questions about the wisdom of Soviet plans as well, whether these were successful or carried the burden of accidents which can occur in the best of programs in any country.

Even if the Soviet Union has put great store in the legend of their space superiority, it is hard to believe an American lunar landing success could have quite the impact on them as did Sputnik on the United States. They have had time to get used to American space accomplishments and their own are sufficiently impressive so that the shock will not be so traumatic.

Now whether the Russians will redouble their efforts in getting men on the moon, or restructure their program objectives in other directions, is harder to judge with certainty. It depends on how important a lunar landing is to their plans. More fundamental is whether they are serious about developing a broad capability to use space. It seems hard to disavow a serious long-term commitment after all that has been said over many years by Soviet authorities. It also would seem hard to hold a different view if a new, very large Soviet vehicle is flown. The hardware associated with large vehicles represents such huge, decade-long investments of time, talent, and resources that it is hardly likely to be abandoned without realizing something on that investment.

ARE SOVIETS QUITTERS?

As far as the United States is concerned, a Soviet manned landing on the moon within the next two or three years may be of less importance than the fact the Soviet Union pursues space flight on a broad front ranging from science and military uses in near Earth space to probes sent to the planets. With or without the intermediate step of a manned landing on the moon (and there is much to commend such practice missions whatever the value of the moon itself), the Soviet Union probably is building toward a wider manned capability for the rest of this century. A permanent manned station in Earth orbit of expanding versatility, leading to an orbital assembly, test, and launch facility for deep space manned flight could in a generation be of greater significance to the relative positions of the great powers than the immediate reaction to the historic first manned landing on the moon, as proud as such an achievement may be.

Essentially, it may be a question of whether the Russians are quitters in the face of adversity. We would judge ourselves as having sufficient resolution in the case of setbacks to move ahead more strongly next time. It is probably wisest to assume the same of the Russian people who for the right or wrong reasons have borne burdens to meet national goals during the last 50 years.

MOSE L. HARVEY

6. THE LUNAR LANDING AND THE U.S.-SOVIET EQUATION

Some discerning wag once said of the Southern Confederacy that its epitaph should read, "Born of States Rights, Died of States Rights." Is it possible that a variant of this will come to be applied to the U.S. commitment to pre-eminence in space: "Born with the Moon Goal, Died with the Moon Goal"? Even with its successful landing on the moon, the United States is in danger of slipping into a position of enduring inferiority as a spacefaring nation.

In calling attention to this paradoxical possibility, I have no thought of subscribing to the view that the moon landing decision constituted some sort of mistake on our part, or has in practice led us into a cul-de-sac. My thought relates instead to the deterioration of national purposefulness with respect to space that has increasingly marked leadership elements within our society as we have progressed toward realization of the moon goal, and even as we now stand at the pinnacle of success.

The moon goal, I would strongly argue, has served the United States well. It has done so not as an end in itself but as part of a process looking toward a far larger end: an enduring position of pre-eminence for the United States in space. In this context, which is the context in which the goal was conceived and against which it was administratively and technically carried forward, the goal reflected American genius and boldness at their best. From the standpoint of what the United States wanted to do in space when the Soviet challenge was fully upon it—what in fact it had to do if it were to avoid lasting damage to its basic national interest—the moon landing was a near ideal focal point around which to organize initial efforts.

Here I would first emphasize an aspect of the matter about which we have recently become somewhat shamefaced: getting ahead of the Russians. The Russians at the opening of the space age had an advantage in booster power that would enable them to best us for many long years in anything we might try to do in the near-Earth environment and in the way of distant probes. But their boosters were not adequate to land men on the moon. The Russians as well as we needed to develop an entirely new booster system. In the race to the moon, we started more or less even. And with our great industrial technological advantages, we had every expectation of success.

TO THE VICTOR . . .

Was it, as some now say, foolish for the United States to think and act in terms of a "race" with the Soviet Union? However the matter may seem to us from the vantage point of our own recent great successes, lunar and martian, it would be well to recall how it was when we had only Soviet successes to look at—when we were faced with the succession of world-wide shockwaves that dealt such devastating blows to both confidence of other peoples in America and confidence of Americans in themselves.

Those, it will be remembered, were the days of near-hysterical soul-searching within this country with regard to the effectiveness of our basic institutions and our way of doing things, even down to the gamut of our educational methods and practices. Those were the days of polls showing that two times as many Italians, three times as many Frenchmen, and four times as many Britishers believed Russia was ahead of America in "scientific development" than the reverse, and that almost as many believed the same way with respect to "the total military power" of the USSR as against the United

States. Those were also the days of the "Sputnik offensive," with its rush of Soviet leaders to gain political advantage from their space exploits, sometimes to the point of playing fast and loose with world peace, as, for example, when Khrushchev sought to intimidate the United States with respect to Cuba in July, 1960:

"It should not be forgotten that the United States is not so inaccessibly distant from the Soviet Union as it used to be. Figuratively speaking, in case of need, Soviet artillerymen can support the Cuban people with their rocket fire if the aggressive forces in the Pentagon dare to launch an intervention against Cuba" (*Pravda*, July 9, 1960).

How would it be with the United States today if we had not mounted a successful effort to challenge Soviet dominance in space? How would it be if Russians and not Americans were the first to walk the surface of the moon and return safely to Earth?

The Soviets have muted their one-time great expectations with regard to their conquest of the moon and what it would mean to them and their world position. But they have done so only as the United States moved toward final success in its own endeavor. As late as March 1966, Yuri Gagarin and co-writer V. I. Lebedev wrote in *Voprosy Filosofii*, the prestigious intellectual journal of the USSR Academy of Sciences:

"The rocket was standing. The explorers appeared to be in a stupor. There was deathly silence. It seemed that they had just awakened from sleep or come to from a faint. At last the Russian got up . . . and said: 'We are on the Moon. . . .' "

"In this way at the dawn of our century K. E. Tsiolkovsky imagined the appearance of the first people on the moon. Now the realization of this great enterprise has very tangibly drawn near. With the successful landing on the moon for the first time of the Soviet automatic station 'Luna-9' one of the next to the last steps was made to the direct landing of cosmonauts on the moon's surface."

SOVIETS ON THE MOON

Common sense tells us of the heights to which Soviet exhilaration, and Soviet world influence, would have mounted and the depths to which American despondency, and American world influence, would have plunged if Russians had indeed been able first to say, "We are on the moon." But leaving entirely aside the matter of a race with the Soviets, a manned moon landing was an eminently worthy first objective for any nation aspiring to a spacefaring role, and indeed for all mankind as it entered the space age. To Earthmen, space, almost by definition, means in the first instance the moon. As men have dreamed over the ages of escaping this planet, they have thought not of tumbling about in a can some hundred or so miles above the Earth's surface, but of going to other planets, and first of all to the moon. And they have dreamed of going themselves, not going by proxy through some machine. For the allure of space has always resided in the promise it holds for an extension of man's domain, not simply his vision. Khrushchev, in his usual earthy way, spoke to President Kennedy at their Vienna meeting about a Russian saying that natural love is better than love through intermediaries. Perhaps this is as good a way as any to put man's feeling about his relationship with space.

Above all else, however, the importance and the genius of the moon project lies in the central role it has played in the build-up of the all-round, basic capabilities of this country to operate in space. From the technical developmental standpoint, as distinct from the political and inspirational, this is what the moon project has been all about. Space strategists, in considering what needed to be done as the United States faced up to the Soviet challenge, saw as crucial: (1) the development of a large multi-purpose booster, (2) a program of activities that would fully explore and test man's ability to live and work in space and under varying conditions and (3) a wide-ranging research and development program capable of extending on an ever-broadening front both scientific knowledge and technological competence with regard to the whole of the space environment and doing jobs in it. While other routes could have been taken to meet these crucial basic needs, the strategists deemed by far the best a concentrated effort to effect a manned landing on the moon. The reasoning that motivated the space people in this was succinctly explained in mid-1961 by NASA (National Aeronautics and Space Administration) Deputy Administrator Hugh Dryden, himself a famed aeronautical scientist:

"The setting of the difficult goal of landing a man on the moon and return to Earth has the highly important role of accelerating the development of space science and technology, motivating the scientists and engineers who are engaged in this effort to move forward with urgency, and integrating their efforts in a way that cannot be accomplished by a disconnected series of research investigations in the several fields. It is important to realize, however, that the real values and purposes are not in the mere accomplishment of man setting foot on the moon, but rather in the great cooperative national effort in the development of space science and technology which is stimulated by this goal."

U.S. CAPABILITIES

What of the capabilities developed with the moon project? What do they add up to? We have:

1. The Saturn V with its 7.5 million pounds of thrust and with a design that will permit adding as an upper stage a nuclear-fueled rocket engine. The Saturn V is a general-purpose workhorse, adequate for the requirements of any of the heavy payload missions that seem at all feasible within the solar system.

2. An assortment of smaller boosters, adaptable to the requirements of the ever-increasing number of specialized jobs that need to be done if the United States is to capitalize on the benefits that space offers for the betterment of life on Earth, as well as for safeguarding and promoting the national security.

3. An array of flight-proved hardware for a variety of missions and activities; tools and other resources to carry on ground-based studies and researches and to do the other things necessary to create new and better hardware and even more ingenious tools; launch, test and support facilities representing a $4 billion investment and adequate to a greatly expanded and even more complex program of space missions than that of the past.

4. The "space teams" encompassing multi-disciplinary elements from industry, universities and the government that constitute what Robert C. Seamans, Jr., former Deputy NASA Administrator and currently Air Force Secretary, characterizes as "the most important base" of U.S. space capability.

5. The truly remarkable organizational and administrative system built up under the aegis of NASA that is demonstrably capable of initiating, developing and exploiting the scientific and technological advances necessary to achieve lasting pre-eminence.

6. The new knowledge and the new operational know-how gained from more than ten years of experience with a multiplicity of jobs that had to be done in order to get us to the moon.

These capabilities, built up as we moved forward with the moon project, represent a wondrous, even awesome, achievement on the part of this country. But that is not the important thing. The important thing is that they represent means in hand that could enable the United States, if it chooses to use and build upon them, to achieve lasting pre-eminence in space.

Some scoff at this idea. They see us trapped with a sort of moon elephant that can serve no other purpose than to repeat over and over a single exercise, or a variant upon it. In fact, what we have is basic to the requirements of any and all of the missions and activities that have been seriously suggested for the next 15 years or so. These include extended manned explorations of the lunar surface; establishing a lunar astronomical observatory, a manned lunar station, and a multi-manned Earth orbiting station; fully developing the range of "space applications" that offer such great promise of economic benefits; systematic explorations of the solar system; a succession of planetary probes and explorations with payloads up to 10,000 pounds; and on down a long list.

Far from having beguiled ourselves into a situation where we have no choice but to do more of the same ("On and On, Up and Up," as *The Economist* has put it), we have, by deliberate design, maintained a striking degree of balance in our activities and efforts. This balance encompasses scientific investigations on a broad front; research and development necessary for a steadily advancing technology applicable to the range of space needs; development and use of a wide array of unmanned as well as increasingly complex manned systems; concentrated and highly rewarding attention to space applications; the conduct of scientific experiments and studies in space by means of both manned and unmanned vehicles; a start on planetary probes; and the simultaneous strengthening of the competence of government research centers, industry and universities to carry forward space assignments and to work effectively together toward common goals.

The problem with regard to our capabilities, indeed with the total of our achievements in space, is not that they are lopsided, or unadaptable to new and increasingly complex jobs, or deficient in some other particular. They are none of these things. One problem is that they are highly perishable unless they are used; they cannot be mothballed, or put on a shelf, or placed on a standby basis. They require a critical mass of activity or they will rapidly disintegrate. But the political decisions have not been reached and, more important, the national resolve has not been engendered that will enable utilization of the capabilities to anything like their full potential. Much momentum has already been lost, and a disintegration process has already set in. Unless we recommit ourselves to a large-scale effort, and this on a broad front involving a balance of activities, and not just within selected areas, this disintegration must necessarily gain speed and leave us in relatively short order with only little to go on or to work with in space.

Hence it is that almost a decade after the United States committed itself to the objective of pre-eminence in space, and at the very moment it stands fully success-ful in the performance of the difficult and complex tasks it set for itself for the 1960s, it finds itself in the strange and paradoxical situation where it is in danger of falling again to second class rank as a spacefaring power.

The circumstance that makes this danger real indeed is that the Soviet Union gives every indication that its own commitment to space is as strong now as ever in the past. We can be sure that Soviet leadership is deeply chagrined at extraordinary American successes. But we can be equally sure that the result will be not a slacken-ing but an expansion and acceleration of the Soviet effort.

SOVIET MOMENTUM

As matters now stand, the USSR has some notable accomplishments of its own, accomplishments involving highly sophisticated and complex capabilities. Its prog-ress toward an Earth orbiting "cosmic station" has reached the payoff stage. It has demonstrated that it has the guidance and other capabilities as well as the hard-ware to carry out manned operations in the vicinity of the moon, and doubtless will soon be able to duplicate, perhaps improve upon, U.S. operations. It now has in hand a new super-booster with thrust one-third to one-half greater than that of Saturn V. On the basis of what is known about the present Soviet situation as compared with the American, it seems almost certain that the USSR will come up with the first manned space station, the first truly maneuverable spacecraft, the first that can be reused for a succession of missions. The Soviets will therefore assume an impressive lead in the early 1970s in planetary and solar probes and exploration.

Overall, the USSR effort has been gaining momentum while the U.S. has been losing. Soviet expenditures on space have been increasing every year since Sputnik I. U.S. expenditures, in contrast, peaked in 1965 and have since been declining, precipitously so in the last three years. There is no parallel in the USSR to the severe cutbacks in skilled work forces, highly trained scientific and technical personnel, and organizational specialists such as have occurred here. And Soviet leaders assert none will take place, as dialogues within the USSR Academy of Sciences testify. The Soviets have had no hiatus, as we have had, in research and development work and preparatory missions in anticipation of programs for the 1970s.

Most striking of all with regard to Soviet purposes is evidence of continued conviction on the part of Soviet leadership that in a full mastery of space lies the key to the attainment of Soviet superiority on a world scale. Sheer prestige and international influence is doubtless a main factor in this. Space has been the one arena in which the USSR led the world, and the Kremlin evidently still savors the heady world acclaim that went with its early space triumphs. Almost certainly, also, the Kremlin has not given up hope that space may somehow yield a military breakthrough and thus an avenue to a quantum jump in strategic power. More than anything else, however, space is looked upon as central to the long-held Soviet aim of attaining world pre-eminence in science and technology.

Among the most fundamental of the Soviet regime's beliefs about its system is that the "socialist mode of production" gives the USSR a decisive advantage in the development and utilization of science and technology to purposeful ends. Illustrative is the assertion in the Party Program of 1961 that "the relations of production under capitalism are much too narrow for a scientific and technical revolution. Socialism alone is capable of effecting it and applying its fruits in the interest of society." While this concept is as old as Marxism and has provided the rationale for Soviet claims, from Lenin on, regarding the certainty of an ultimate Soviet triumph, it remained largely a matter of faith until the USSR mounted its space successes. Then faith changed to conviction.

Typical of the Soviet point of view is the assertion in the "Theses" for the 1967 celebration of the fiftieth anniversary of the Bolshevik Revolution: "Our scientific achievements find their concentrated expression in the study and conquest of the cosmos." To this might be added such statements as that of Soviet Party Secretary B. N. Ponomarev at the Congress of the Italian Communist Party in February, 1969: "All the new successes in the conquest of space are a symbol of the technological achievements of the Soviet people. . . . We can assure you that the list of our achievements in space will be extended!" Soviet thinking, even more than American, is in terms of a direct linkage between space achievements and a general upsurge in science and technology and a corresponding increase (through maximum "scientification of production") in the overall strength of the USSR.

SOVIET OBJECTIVES

The Soviets quite evidently have expected more in the way of concrete returns from their space-centered advances in science and technology than they have been able to realize. This has led in the past several years to a spate of self-criticism and a considerable amount of thrashing about in search of better means of organizing and administering scientific activities in the interest of greater utilitarian results. Yet the leaders have not wavered in their conviction that science and technology hold the key to the realization of their objectives at home and abroad or in their conviction that the "socialist mode of production" is inherently superior to the "capitalist mode." Their posture is that greater rather than lessened emphasis on science and technology is called for, but within an organizational framework that will more effectively than in the past capitalize on the "advantages" offered by the socialist mode.

V. A. Trapeznikov, Deputy Chairman of the Soviet

State Committee on Science and Technology, well reflected the Soviet reasoning in *Izvestiya* of October 25, 1968: "In contemporary conditions the tempo of technological progress becomes the decisive factor in the competition of the two world systems. . . ." So too did M. V. Keldysh, president of the USSR Academy of Sciences, at the annual general meeting of the Academy in March 1969: "Technological progress is now the determining factor . . . for the development of the socialist economy. In the plans for the development of the national economy, particularly in the next Five-Year Plan, special attention will be given to increasing the tempo of technological progress." And in a follow-up *Pravda* article of March 15, 1969: "Each scientist must become imbued with the understanding that the future of our country and the creation of the material-technical base of communism depend to a large extent on the effectiveness of science. Science must assist effectively in the future not only peaceful construction but also the strengthening of the defense of our Motherland."

And from the authoritative voice of Premier Kosygin at a Party Conference at Minsk in February 1968: ". . . in the development of science lies the future of our country, the growth of our economy and the sharp rise of the standard of living of the population. . . . Scientific and technological progress exerts a tremendous influence on labor productivity and the achievements of our science and technology in the area of production of contemporary machinery and equipment, and the assimilation of the newest technological processes are unquestionable . . . ."

The Soviets have backed up their faith in science and technology as the key to their future by steadily increasing their rate of investment in the area, including, as the *Bulletin of the USSR Academy of Sciences* emphasized in June, 1968, "the priority role of . . . science and technology in . . . cosmic research." Since Sputnik I, investments in science and technology have increased at an annual rate varying from eight to 14 per cent. Investments in 1968 were three times as great as in 1958 (nine billion rubles as against three billion) and were several times as much as expenditures on higher education. (It should be noted that these figures apply to research and development activities exclusive of hardware procurement, as required, for example, for the space program.) At the same time Soviet leaders have emphasized that in their view investments in science and technology yield far greater returns than investments in other fields, and have been unequivocal in expressing their intent to continue to increase investments in sicence and technology over the indefinite future, even at the expense of investments in capital equipment expansion. Given current trends in the United States, the sort of things Soviet leaders are saying appear to merit close attention: Kosygin at the Minsk Oblast Party Conference in February 1968: "We will systematically increase allocations for the development of science and scientific research. . . ."

V. A. Trapeznikov in an article in the *Ekonomicheskaya Gazeta* of July 1968: "A ruble invested in science and the assimilation of its results give 1.45 rubles of growth in the national income. On the other hand, the growth of national income from the usual capital investments comprises 39 kopeks for the invested ruble. Consequently, expenditures on science and the assimilation of its results are approximately 3.5 times more effective than the usual capital investments. Since investments in science are particularly effective, it is advisable to reduce somewhat the [usual] capital investments and to give the released resources to science and the assimilation of its results. . . . In accordance with our calculations we should increase expenditures on science two times."

Pravda of February 4, 1969, in a lead editorial article entitled "Science—the Productive Force of Society" ". . . investment in science is a most profitable matter . . . a ruble of expenditure on 'science and development' gives an increase in national income almost four times greater than investment in expanding production capital in the absence of technical progress [i.e., without using up-to-date technology]."

NO TIME TO RELAX

The United States can ill afford to ignore or discount either what the Soviets are doing in space and in support of space-related science and technology, or the reasons for which they are doing it. Americans have long had a way of becoming aroused by an unexpected Soviet accomplishment, mounting a major counter-effort of our own in response, and then, as we ourselves achieve spectacular successes, relaxing amidst the ensuing euphoria, rather than looking objectively at either long-term Soviet trends or our own long-term interests. This habit has gotten us into some ticklish situations in the past. It could get us into a real jam as the challenges and requirements of the space age fully unfold.

George Simpson, Chancellor of the University System of Georgia, sees the implications in these terms: "Down through the course of history, the mastery of a new environment, or of a major new technology, or of the combination of the two as we now see in space, has had profound effects on the future of nations; on their relative strength and security; on their relations with one another; on their internal economic, social and political affairs; and on the concepts of reality held by their people."

It is questionable whether any nation, even one as richly endowed as the United States, can long continue as a great power if it concedes to others primacy in such a sphere as space. No one can know with certainty the total of the gains that can be realized from the mastery of the space environment. But a scant dozen years ago no one knew with certainty that anything at all could be done in space: whether enough power could be generated to get a body into orbit; whether a man could survive the thrust into space or under conditions of weightlessness; whether escape from the Earth's environment was barred by lethal radiation belts; whether the moon's surface was so layered with dust as to smother any craft attempting to land; whether rendezvous and

docking were possible; whether anything useful could be
learned about the weather, or about the surface of the
Earth and the phenomena that affect it. Learned men
have differed over these and many other things about
which we now know with surety. But we have come to
know things with surety only as we have penetrated and
explored and tested. So too will it be with the other
things about which we still question and conjecture and
differ. The full meaning of space for men and for nations, now and for the future, will be determined only
as one nation or another continues to go and see and
learn what is actually there and what can be done with it.

The stakes for the United States go beyond the dimensions that have traditionally weighted the balance sheet
of strengths and weaknesses and prospects of one nation
as against others. They extend into dimensions peculiar
to our times, dimensions that relate to the rapidly accelerating scientific-technological revolution, dimensions
that are enlarging and becoming more determinant at an
exponential rate.

THE KNOWLEDGE CAPITAL

Fundamental to all else is the matter of knowledge.
Knowledge has become the most decisive resource available to any nation. The United States has become the
knowledge capital of the world. A single statistic will
illustrate: Since 1940 U.S. nationals have received more
Nobel prizes in the sciences than the nationals of all
other countries of the world combined. In almost every
field these days anyone from any part of the globe who
wants to get at the forefront of knowledge and the new
discoveries in knowledge has to look first and last to the
United States.

Even the Russians currently make a point of the superiority of the United States in the acquisition of
knowledge. Soviet Academician Peter L. Kapitsa told the
USSR Academy of Sciences in 1965: ". . . They [the
Americans] now produce about one-third of world science. We produce one-sixth of world science, that is
twice less than they. Each of the remaining countries

produces less than we. Therefore in scientific production we are the second country in the world. However, if one takes into account . . . [that the numbers of American and Soviet scientists are approximately equal] then it appears that with approximately the same number of scientific workers we produce half of the scientific work which the Americans produce. . . . The productivity of our scientists is approximately two times lower than the productivity of the scientists of the USA."

Assume that the United States does not continue to match the USSR in its efforts to explore and master space with its wondrous opportunities to advance and enlarge knowledge and understanding: How long can the United States hope to retain its leadership as a producer and user of knowledge? How long will it remain the knowledge capital of the world? Here three circumstances would appear worthy of sober reflection: (1) The United States has attained its position of world leadership as a producer of knowledge only quite recently—with World War II and its aftermath. (To use again the Nobel statistic as an indicator: Prior to the outbreak of World War II, Americans received less than one-fourth as many Nobel Prizes in science as Germans, and less than one-tenth as many as Europeans taken together; among all nations, the United States was a poor fourth to France.) (2) Scientific and technical progress during the contemporary period has been overwhelmingly dependent on massive endeavors undertaken and supported by governments. (3) For a span of several years America stood on the verge of losing its position as knowledge leader. When Sputnik brought the opening of the space age, the Soviet Union and not the United States was the knowledge capital for space and all that related to space. Russians and not Americans spoke with authority for space, and to Russians and not Americans turned the world scientific community, including the scientific community of the U.S. itself, to learn about that new frontier area of human knowledge. More than that, much of the world community felt that Russians had attained overall knowledge leadership, as witness the polls re-

ferred to above. That the situation has changed has been
largely due to U.S. space and related successes. Had we
not mounted our own effort to achieve space preeminence, or been less bold or effective in carrying the effort
forward, Americans might already be well along the road
toward enduring eclipse as creators of knowledge.

There is a reverse side of this matter which, while
subtle and elusive, is fraught with far-reaching implications: the growing impact of U.S.-Soviet competition in
science and technology, particularly as it relates to space,
to the social values and world outlook of the Soviet intellectual elite.

SOVIET SCIENTISTS QUESTION . . .

During recent years, deep stirrings have marked Soviet
scientific circles. The stimulus has come principally from
the regime-encouraged search for greater effectiveness in
Soviet scientific and technological work. However, as
Soviet scientists have looked at themselves, and exam-
ined ways to achieve improvements, their inquiry has
tended to broaden into a quest for a more rational society
in which to live and work and for more constructive and
less dangerous relationships with the outside world.

Andrei Sakharov, a Soviet physicist of many accomplishments and great prestige, gave indication of the
nature and extent of what is going on in the remarkable
essay he circulated more or less openly among his colleagues in June of last year: ". . . the scientific and scientific-technological intelligentsia . . . manifests much
anxiety over the principles and specific aspects of foreign
and domestic policy and over the future of mankind."
Concerns, he explained, relate to such considerations as
these: "The division of mankind threatens it with
destruction. . . . Any action increasing the division of
mankind, any preaching of the incompatibility of world
ideologies and nations is madness and a crime . . . intellectual freedom is essential to human society—freedom
to obtain and distribute information, freedom for open-
minded and unfearing debate and freedom from pressure
by officialdom and prejudices."

Sakharov's own views as developed in this essay go further, are expressed more starkly, and are more directly oriented toward the international scene than others that have surfaced in the Soviet Union. (The essay has been published in full by the New York Times under the title Progress, Coexistence and Intellectual Freedom [New York: W. W. Norton, 1968].) Nevertheless, insofar as fundamentals are concerned, they reflect a fairly broad and obviously growing trend within the scientific community. Not only have there been frequent instances where views in keeping with Sakharov's have been voiced in conversations and group discussions and in privately circulated documents, but even in material published in professional journals and books. An example of the latter that is particularly Sakharov-like in tone appeared in Voprosy Filosofii in June, 1966:

"The unheard of power attained by contemporary science which [if] applied for destructive purposes creates a real threat of the destruction of civilization, and perhaps of life itself on our planet, and on the other hand the dependence of further scientific-technological progress on intelligent organization of society force one to think about such questions as the social function of science, the responsibility of scientists to society, the place of science and technology in the life of society, the influence of social-economic conditions on the tempo and direction of scientific-technological development, etc. . . . It would be beneficial if deeper study . . . acquainted [responsible leaders] with some basic principles: the danger of sacrificing pure research for applied . . .; the necessity to encourage personal initiative; . . . the disastrous influence on scientific creativity of all dogmas . . . and also of political censorship, exercised sometimes by some scientists possessing too great administrative power. . . ."

The backdrop against which Soviet scientists are appraising their situation and identifying their needs is America: What Americans are doing, how they are doing it, why they are having greater success than the Soviets themselves. They are being told, as by a Voprosy

Filosofii editorial of June 1968, that "production relations of socialism and capitalism create different conditions for the scientific-technological revolution and cause not only different but in many ways opposite consequences." But many evidently do not believe what they are being told and increasingly resist its implications. They give no indication of any yen for "capitalism" as such, nor do they show any dissatisfaction with "socialism" as such. But the concept that ideological considerations ordain an unabridgeable gulf between science and technology under the one system as against the other, or that they make necessarily different conditions of work and different consequences, appears to be something else again.

THE SOCIALIST MODE

Also, and this would seem most important, Soviet scientists are demonstrably having increasing difficulty reconciling in their own minds the dogma of the superiority of the socialist mode of production, which is so fundamental to the objectives and policies of the regime, with the objective realities of the Soviet situation in science and technology, as against the American. Sakharov states the matter bluntly: "There are no grounds for asserting . . . that the capitalist mode of production leads a country into a blind alley or that it is inherently inferior to the socialist mode. . . ."

All of this is, of course, in marked contrast to the confident state of mind that prevailed among Soviet scientists during the short years in which the USSR stood alone as a conqueror of space.

Whether the trend toward a new and different orientation within the ranks of the Soviet scientific-technological elite will produce meaningful results can only be conjectured. Past experiences suggest the need for caution. People in the West have all too often found willo'-the-wisps where they thought they were finding confirmation of their ingrained belief that the educated, and particularly the scientifically and technically educated, would someday, somehow assert themselves as against the ideologues in the USSR and get the Soviet system on a basis more compatible with their own standards. Yet, considering the far-reaching implications, the United States would seem to have a rather large stake in having the trend run as long and as strongly as possible.

This, however, ties in with another area of conjecture that is quite critical. Will the American way continue in fact to prove more effective than the Soviet? The issue here need not be confused with jargon about modes of production. It revolves around the simple but crucial matter of willingness to stay the course. It centers on the question of the consequences if the United States stood back and allowed the USSR new triumphs in space comparable to the Sputnik triumph, or a succession of such triumphs.

The moon landing has resulted in a renewal of impetus to the U.S. space effort. Some log jams of several years' duration have been broken and activities gotten under way that insure the program will not grind to an early halt. But the larger issue of whether the United States is to recommit itself to the scale of effort and the range of activities and for the sustained time period that are necessary to keep it pre-eminent in space has not been resolved.

PUBLIC VS. PRIVATE PURPOSES

What are the prospects that this larger issue will be resolved in a manner to safeguard for now and for the indefinite future the vital interests of the United States? The answer would seem to lie in whether we can, at long last, end what Adlai Stevenson called "the quarrel between public and private purposes." This quarrel, which extends deep into our history, is now raging with almost unprecedented bitterness around "the military-industrial complex." It may soon extend to the so far muted second half of Eisenhower's warning: ". . . the danger that public policy could . . . become a captive of a scientific and technological elite."

The capability of the United States to continue in

space, and otherwise to keep pace with the scientific-technological revolution, depends entirely on continued public faith in the "military-industrial complex" and the "scientific and technological elite," if one wishes to keep using these unfortunate terms. It was only because we were able effectively to organize and use a genuine and mutually rewarding partnership between industry, universities and government that we were able to effect the moon landing and to do the other near-miraculous things we have done in space and in other fields involving advanced science and advanced technology. It is precisely on this partnership that the superiority of the American way over the Soviet way has so far rested. And it is precisely on our ability to maintain the partnership and to strengthen it and maximize its use as a matter of course that our future effectiveness, in comparison with the USSR, will receive its deciding test.

PHILIP M. SMITH

7. PROSPECTS FOR INTERNATIONAL COOPERATION ON THE MOON: THE ANTARCTIC ANALOGY

There has been much recent discussion of analogies between exploration and research in Antarctica and the lunar exploration that has begun. And there are indeed many parallels in the objective for basic research in the geophysical sciences, transportation, construction techniques, search and rescue problems and in program management. In Antarctica and in lunar research the motivation is the pursuit of knowledge; no exploitable economic resources will provide economic benefit in the near future. But no analogy between the lunar program and the existing program in Antarctica is of greater interest than a comparison of cooperation among nations working in Antarctica, especially the Soviet Union and the United States, and the possibilities for similar cooperation on the moon and in lunar research in the decades ahead. Scientific cooperation in Antarctica did not come about quickly or easily. In the lunar case, it cannot be expected to be an immediate development. Instead, if the Antarctic analogy is valid, we must believe that international cooperation in lunar exploration and research will not be realized until the 1980s and 1990s. Then man will have moved from an early exploratory period into an era where there is more sophisticated lunar operational capability and where scientific reasons for conducting a long-term program of lunar study are more evident than they are today.

Antarctica is now known as a continent of interna-

85

tional harmony among the countries working there, and it is a continent noted for its cooperation in the pursuit of basic research. Neither international harmony nor sustained year-round scientific expeditions are pursuits that have long been a part of Antarctic history—the opposite is the case. Until the end of the 1950s dispute over conflicting national claims and the pursuit of expedition objectives that might substantiate national interests were major reasons for exploration activities in Antarctica. Exploration of the continent derived from national and commercial interests rather than international objectives. Moreover, scientific research on many of the national exploratory expeditions was an ancillary rather than a primary goal.

THE HEROIC AGE

Although Captain James Cook and other eighteenth century voyagers searched for the broad outlines of a southern continental land mass, the first important coastal explorations in Antarctica were made by sealers. They were most active in the vicinity of the Antarctic Peninsula, an area of Antarctica generally accessible to ships not equipped with ice-strengthened hulls or ice-breaking characteristics. Scientists participated in some sealing expeditions with frustration that was attendant on the pursuit of seals instead of science. James Eights, an Albany, New York geologist, accompanying an 1829 voyage, returned home to express the opinion that a nation with a "population whose daring enterprise had already carried . . . [the] flag into the remotest corners of the globe" would be lax if it did not carry out an Antarctic expedition, "the expense of which would little exceed that of a vessel doubling Cape Horn." When the seals were fully exploited, in the 1830s, attention turned to whales, a pursuit which led man away from the continent instead of onto it.

National expeditions, meanwhile, were occasionally mounted: by Russia (1820) and France, Great Britain and America (1839–41). These expeditions worked their way along considerable portions of the Antarctic coastline, making significant geographical discoveries and scientific observations. That these were national enterprises is illustrated by the fact that at the international conference on Antarctica in 1959, each of these nations cited its expedition in the 1800s as a historical interest in the continent and as a "right" or precedent for participation in a meeting to draft an international treaty.

A foothold on the continent itself was achieved at the turn of the century, when Antarctica's "heroic era" began. The heroic era was in actuality the nationalistic age. It opened with the expeditions of Nordenskjöld, Scott and Amundsen and continued through the expeditions of Byrd, Ellsworth and Ritscher, whose Schwabenland expedition immediately before the outbreak of World War II was a German thrust into the icy continent. The largest expedition ever mounted to Antarctica, the U.S. "Operation High Jump" in 1947, and the establishment of permanent stations by Argentina, Australia, Chile, France and the United Kingdom, which support their claims to portions of the continent, brought the final phase of Antarctica's national history toward its end.

The intense rivalry and competition between nations in Antarctica during the heroic age are well known and characterized most often by the Amundsen-Scott race to the South Pole during the 1911–1912 austral summer. Less well known are the many rivalries which existed between Argentina, Chile and Great Britain on the Antarctic Peninsula between the close of World War II and the signing of the Antarctic Treaty in 1959. These grew out of conflicting, overlapping territorial claims on the Peninsula. A firing with rifles upon a British party by Argentines at Hope Bay could be said to have been pro forma in execution of orders from foreign offices thousands of miles distant from Antarctica. It is true that the notes of protest concerning the "occupancy" of the other nation's territory, issued at irregular intervals in this period, were often followed by festive camaraderie among the expedition members once the pro forma obligations were concluded. These protests, nonetheless, represented official national viewpoints at the time.

TECHNIQUES EXPAND

Throughout this period of national exploration techniques of travel and living constantly improved. Scientific objectives were given strong support at the turn of the century when the heroic age began, but as transportation into the continental interior and ease of living at established stations along the Antarctic coast grew, more ambitious science was planned. Projects which could be carried out became more apparent also as the geographical knowledge of the southern continent increased. The massive accomplishments of "Operation High Jump" in aerial photography and the work of the several nations with semi-permanent stations pointed out many problems that could only be studied in longer-term science programs.

Antarctica's international history truly began with the Norwegian-British-Swedish expedition (1949–1952). This expedition was of great significance: It seriously proposed a cooperative venture among the scientists of three nations, undertaking many studies such as glaciology with the utilization of new equipment and instrumentation, all on an order of magnitude more sophisticated than that used on many earlier expeditions. The cooperation among these three nations developed a model that was useful in the consideration of the Antarctic cooperation to be developed during the International Geophysical Year (IGY). Antarctica was not exclusively a reason for the development of the IGY, but the then widespread knowledge that many scientific problems—both within Antarctica, as in geology and glaciology, and as Antarctica could be used as a platform for study of solar-terrestrial phenomena—contributed greatly to the strong international support given the IGY Antarctic program. Moreover, leading scientists and administrators in several of the nations proposing work in Antarctica had had an earlier experience at a time when basic research had not been so favorably received by either the financial backers of the private exploratory ventures or the expedition members in the heroic age.

In the United States, Lloyd V. Berkner and Laurence M. Gould, both members of the 1928 Byrd expedition, lent Antarctic experience and their academic and administrative prestige to the international developments of the IGY.

The IGY cooperation in Antarctica with one notable exception was primarily a cooperation in which each nation independently contributed its national program to an international scientific plan. The participating nations constructed their own bases, provided their own scientists and prepared their own scientific results, which were forwarded as national contributions to data centers established for the IGY. The one important exception was establishment of a weather central at the U.S. Little America Station. Scientists from the Argentine, Australia, France, New Zealand, South Africa, the United States and the Soviet Union worked in cooperation and in harmony on the joint analysis and reduction of data over two years.

Cooperation in logistics among nations in Antarctica ensued in the IGY. Most often this took the form of logistic assistance when the expedition of another nation ran into difficulty, such as heavy sea-ice conditions that necessitated relief by powerful icebreakers. A network for telecommunications was established with reporting "daughter" stations broadcasting to central collective points or "mother" stations without regard to nationality. A prime user of the telecommunication network was the Little America weather central.

SOVIET-U.S. ANTARCTIC COOPERATION

By the end of the IGY, scientific reasons for a continuing program in Antarctica were self-evident. Instead of definitively answering questions, many of the studies, such as the glaciological oversnow traverses that measured the thickness of the Antarctic ice cap, led to the conclusion that further studies must be initiated. Recognizing that scientific cooperation should continue, the Antarctic IGY organizing committee reconstituted itself as the Scientific Committee on Antarctic Research

(SCAR) under the aegis of the International Council of Scientific Unions. The continued scientific dialog among interested nations was thus assured. Meanwhile, as a political initiative, the United States issued an invitation to other nations which had participated in the IGY to explore ways in which they could reach "agreement among themselves on a program to insure the continuation of the fruitful scientific cooperation after the end of the IGY." The conference on Antarctica in 1959 led to the now well known Antarctic Treaty which was ratified in 1961. Some 60 years after the first national expeditions that wintered, the international and scientific elements of Antarctic operations truly emerged as the reasons for maintaining somewhat costly outposts at the bottom of the Earth.

The cooperative activities that have been carried out among all nations in the last 10 years are numerous. Of special interest from the context of this article is cooperation between the Soviet Union and the United States, for successes and failures in this cooperative context bear on future lunar exploration and research. Each nation has had a long-standing historical interest in Antarctica, although neither was especially active in Antarctica nationally for a period of about 100 years while others were exploring the continent. Unlike seven nations which made claims, neither USSR nor the United States has made a territorial claim or recognized those made. And each has established itself logistically with the most comprehensive array of transportation tools ranging from large oversnow tractors to aircraft. Only the Soviet Union and the United States maintain stations scattered across the whole continent. The Soviet Union has four major stations on the coast and one inland, Vostok, located near the geomagnetic pole. The United States maintains three coastal stations, and two in the continental interior—Byrd and the Amundsen-Scott South Pole Station.

In science, cooperation has centered on the exchange of scientists between the expeditions. Each year since 1957, with one exception, there has been an annual exchange, for the wintering period, of Soviet and U.S. scientists. These exchanges have been in all scientific disciplines, with geology, biology, meteorology and upper atmosphere sciences being the most frequent. On one occasion oceanographers were exchanged. The American ship *Eltanin* carried a Soviet oceanographer for a 60-day cruise and a U.S. scientist participated in a cruise of the Soviet research ship *Ob*. The stations selected for the winter exchanges are generally related to the investigators' planned work. As the exchange is not a quid pro quo arrangement by scientific discipline there may in one year be an American biologist at a Soviet coastal station and a Russian atmospheric physicist at a U.S. ice-cap station. At this writing an atmospheric physicist from the Environmental Science Services Administration is wintering at Vostok and a Russian aviation meteorologist is wintering at McMurdo. The two men pursue their own programs in the context of the other station activities and maintain occasional radio contact with each other to exchange pleasantries and notes on being the sole representatives of their countries in an unfamiliar culture for a period of a year.

Many of the exchanges have been those in which facilities and transportation of the counterpart nation have been made available. On rare occasions there has been a cooperation that has extended to an analysis and publication of the data. It seems likely that this cooperation in publication, which results in true fusion of scientific thought by investigators in the two countries, will become an increasing part of future programs. Currently, V. P. Hessler of the University of Alaska and Madam V. A. Troitskaya, Soviet Academy of Sciences, are undertaking a joint analysis and publication of atmospheric studies. The Soviet Union and the United States, together with France and Australia, are discussing a 10-year program of glaciological research in East Antarctica that would begin in 1970. The International Antarctic Glaciological Project (IAGP), as it is called, will study in greater detail than has been done a million-square-mile portion of the ice cap. IAGP undoubtedly will lead to further cooperation in joint field work and publication of data.

LOGISTIC COOPERATION

On several occasions logistic assistance has been provided for Soviet aircraft at the U.S. McMurdo Station and for U.S. aircraft at the Russian station, Mirnyy. Flights have been made by the United States to Vostok each of the last five summers. In the IAGP it is likely that this logistic cooperation will expand, with aircraft of both nations operating for periods of time from the other nation's air facilities instead of transiting these airfields as in the past. Search and rescue assistance has also taken place. In one instance Soviet and U.S. teams combined effort to provide assistance to an ailing Australian scientist who was flown by the Soviets from the Australian Mawson to the U.S. McMurdo Station for further air transportation by the Americans to New Zealand where major hospital facilties were available. In April 1961, a historic winter flight was made to Byrd Station by a U.S. plane to retrieve the wintering Soviet exchange scientist, then suffering from a severe gastrointestinal disorder. In 1967 when a U.S. aircraft which had lost radio contact with the U.S. stations became overdue, Soviet officials at Vostok provided assistance in identifying the track of the aircraft.

In both the logistic and scientific exchange between U.S. and Soviet Antarctic expeditions there have been barriers that have not been overcome. One of these is language. The exchange scientists, of course, learn language quickly, sometimes in a sink-or-swim fashion. On the intergovernmental levels for scientific and logistic planning there still remain barriers which can be attributed to a no more deeply held motive than puzzlement over meaning in translation. The interpretation of the basic language and the accurate translation of idom have required a patience and understanding which has slowly developed over the years of cooperation. Even so, certain difficulties are experienced. Absence of a reply to a proposal cannot be taken at first glance as a lack of interest in the proposal's merit; it may result from a lack of understanding of the proposal itself. A second, more serious difficulty is the impingement of world conflict and tension. On Antarctica, these tensions are virtually nonexistent. Exchange scientists have weathered well during the U-2 episode, the Cuban missile crisis and the invasion of Czechoslovakia. Moreover, there have been official inspections of the Soviet stations by the United States under the terms of the Antarctic Treaty, carried out with a guarded but cordial harmony.

Though the organizing officials in both nations have been very successful in freeing Antarctic cooperation which results from this larger context of friction between the nations. For example, discussion of the further or continuing exchange of the Antarctic scientists to the laboratories and facilities of the host nations on completion of the year in Antarctica tends to become embroiled in the quid pro quo arrangements for travel, cultural exchange and so on. Several years ago a Congressional committee berated a U.S. Antarctic program official for providing fuel to Soviet aircraft without cost, overlooking the fact that reciprocal refueling of U.S. aircraft had taken place at Mirnyy. These problems are not consistent with the spirit of cooperation that has been engendered on the Antarctic continent but they are a part of official life on both sides. A third problem with the U.S.-USSR cooperation has been a problem inherent in science itself. Though the concept of international cooperation is now clearly a part of science, there often remains in the heart of many investigators an understandable desire to have first priority over significant or "cream of the crop" results. The language barriers, the mode of publication and lost time in correspondence are cited rather than personal desire for recognition in working up of data. These are contributing factors but they cannot be considered truly significant since the national programs require many workers and great national investment, transcending the old concept of the professor experimenting in his laboratory. One must have a commitment to international science and cooperation to make it work. It remains a fact that many scientists are not yet prepared to work in an international context.

STAGES IN LUNAR COOPERATION

The present achievements in Antarctica have come about from a long and historically complicated period of exploration and research. It is true that in the case of international cooperation in space and on the moon certain great advantages should make cooperation possible at a much earlier time than this cooperation was possible in Antarctica. Most important, a treaty on outer space, drawing much from the Antarctic Treaty, predates man's reaching the moon, establishing a framework for cooperation before the scientific work is done instead of after much of it was started, as in Antarctica. The geographical description of the moon was nearly complete before the first manned landings. In Antarctica, the continuing exploration extended to and beyond the IGY and the signing of the Treaty. Thus two apparent causes for noncooperation, uncertainty about the geography of the moon and its political status, are vastly different from the Antarctic situation as it existed in the IGY and immediate post-IGY era.

Nonetheless, there is no cause for optimism concerning lunar cooperation between the Soviet Union and the United States at this time. Three fundamental prerequisites are yet to be met. They are the satisfaction of nationlism in exploration, the development of lunar operational capabilities, and discovery of scientific reasons for conducting long-term programs on the moon.

Nationalism will continue to be associated with exploration for many years just as it has been in the past.

It is difficult to imagine an exchange scientist program between the Amundsen and Scott parties. In the context of the present lunar exploration program it is difficult to imagine cooperation between astronauts and cosmonauts. Indeed the undesirability of such cooperation has been noted by both the spacemen and by politicians who went so far as to amend a NASA appropriation bill to insure that the U.S. flag was erected on the moon. In the

Soviet Union one suspects that the same national fervor for the moon may exist. While it is true that widespread cooperation is planned in the analysis of the first lunar samples and that there are other measures for cooperation (such as aid to astronauts) one must be realistic about the matter of nationalism. The nationalistic fervor associated with reaching the moon must be vented before international objectives can be seriously proposed. It is not at all certain that the nationalistic spirit of competition will be met by the early manned missions. The high cost of the ongoing lunar missions and the tremendous investment in manned space systems will be remembered by taxpayers and politicians long after the historic first landing on the moon. These expenditures tend to make the man on the street in our society possessive rather than international in outlook. Historically, a nationalistic approach to exploration has sustained such adventures for some time after the initial discoveries or conquests, and in the lunar analogy this should be expected also.

Our operational capability in Antarctica was truly demonstrated in "Operation High Jump." With it, technical and equipment development gave scienitsts greater mobility and freedom of access to the areas of their specific interest. We are now at about the same stage in our lunar operational capability as the explorers who landed in Antarctica in the early 1800s. Between the first Antarctic coastal landings and the first year-round stations after 1900, there were many brief visits, but no sustained operations. Though the moon has been reached, an operational capabilitv on it is far from being realized. Transportation systems for extensive lunar exploration and the capability for increased sojourns in semi-permanent lunar bases will be necessary before it will be possible to entertain cooperation which takes place on the moon as it does today in Antarctica.

Proposals are made from time to time to the effect that the technological capabilities of the two nations should be merged into a joint space exploration. This is a marvelous ideal. Given the existing international context, however, it appears impractical to entertain such thoughts at least until after semi-permanent manned stations are a reality.

SUSTAINED EXPLORATION

A third most important deterrent to immediate Soviet-U.S. cooperation is that scientific reasons for sustained lunar exploration are not yet clearly evident. Scientists suspect that there are many long-term investigations to be carried out, but these needs will not be demonstrated completely until there has been an initial period of exploration, such as that which is proposed in the follow-on Apollo landings of the 1970s. Until more is known scientifically about the moon, cooperation in investigations may be slow in developing. A lesson to be drawn from the Antarctic is important here. Where there have been soundly conceived scientific problems, cooperative arrangements among the scientists of the several nations have tended to suggest themselves. Where the scientific justification for cooperation in Antarctica has been slim, cooperation has not been good, no matter how strongly officialdom may want it to take place. Slowly emerging but totally self-sustaining scientific arguments for lunar cooperation will manifest themselves in time.

A TIMETABLE

These deterrents to international cooperation in the lunar context do not mean cooperation will not take place, for indeed it will. When there is an understanding on both sides of the scientific problems to be solved, when nationalistic requirements have been met by both nations' flights to the moon, and when sufficient and safe station and transportation systems have been developed, cooperation between the Soviet and U.S. expeditions could begin in earnest. Assuming Soviet space motives include a long-term program of lunar study, a timetable for Soviet-U.S. cooperation on the moon can be drawn from the Antarctic experience. This timetable has three major phases. The first phase will include expeditions to the moon by both nations with missions determined on the basis of national estimates of priority. A number of such missions can be imagined as both nations will exploit the costly manned mission systems independently developed. A growing cooperation in the exchange of data during this phase can be anticipated, and both nations will utilize the expeditions as means of developing cooperation in data analysis within the context of Earthbound political considerations within their power blocks. Near the end of this phase increased coordination in mission planning can be expected, for example in the selection of traverse routes for manned missions and lunar roving research vehicles operating in an unmanned mode.

The second phase of lunar cooperation will occur when increased sojourns become a reality, and semi-permanent lunar bases are planned. Cooperation in mission planning will be extended to include coordinated site selection for manned lunar laboratories. Base construction, however, will proceed independently by each nation. Though the technologies in the two national programs will be quite similar, hardware development will be dependent on the differing national industrial systems. Increasing attention will be given to data centers and exchange of scientific data, for the investigations which justify semi-permanent lunar laboratories will result in ever-increasing amounts of data. Initially little cooperation which involves the exchange of scientists can be expected in the second phase, for lunar scientists will still require extensive training as space pilots. But by the end of the second phase, serious plans will have been drawn for the cooperative manning of lunar stations. Exchanges of individual scientists will begin. Also scientists from nations not possessing manned space systems will be trained by both the USSR and the United States for their lunar stations. In this phase long distance lunar transportation systems will have become perfected to the point that interdependence for lunar search and rescue will become effective. The planning of expeditions will also give some attention to opportunities for lunar visits between stations and field parties for life-support systems will have been developed sufficiently to permit such luxury in lunar living.

THE THIRD PHASE

In the third phase truly cooperative programs between the Soviet Union and the United States at all levels—cooperative missions in space flight, jointly manned lunar research centers, and cooperation in data analysis—will take place. This complete cooperation in lunar work may precede in all probability such complete interdependence in the Antarctic operations. The extreme costs and the great human hazards inherent in space flight will force an internationalization not yet realized in Antarctica. At this point in time, Mars will have been reached and manned missions to the more distant bodies of the solar system will have been initiated. Lunar cooperation between the Soviet Union and the United States will be taken then as a model for other space activity, just as Antarctic cooperation today may serve as a model for suggesting cooperation on the moon.

WILLIAM LEAVITT

8. POST-APOLLO POLICY: A LOOK INTO THE 1970S

Although it is by no means the highest-priority item on President Nixon's agenda, the post-Apollo future of the U.S. space program, debated fitfully in and out of government circles for many months now, is beginning to get some of the administration's attention. If the presently discernible policy trends mature into action, the 1970s could be a decade of space applications, with the emphasis more on societal benefits and less on spectacular achievements geared to prestige.

Not long after the President took office, his science advisor, Dr. Lee DuBridge, former president of the California Institute of Technology, launched a study of the requirements for a balanced U.S. space program for the next 10 years that would produce early benefits for Earthbound man while at the same time advancing scientific knowledge of the near space around the Earth and providing more data on the moon and the planets. Dr. DuBridge's task force report is supposed to be completed in September 1969. Meanwhile, Dr. DuBridge and others in the administration, including the leadership of NASA (National Aeronautics and Space Administration), have had the opportunity to study such items as the recent report of a large and distinguished panel of specialists in disciplines ranging from communications to hydrology, organized by the National Academy of Sciences (NAS), National Academy of Engineering (NAE), and the National Research Council (NRC) to examine the potential of an extensive unmanned application satellite program for the years ahead. The NAS-NAE-NRC group, in their final report, came out strongly for a much more vigorous unmanned Earth-satellite program to extract data and benefits in a broad array of fields including Earth-resources survey, weather-watching, and data management, among others. Even more significantly, the panel urged that applications satellites and their potential benefits not be justified in the context of manned space-flight. That tendency has been quite strong in recent years in planning circles at NASA, caught up as the space agency has been in the excitement of the Apollo manned lunar landing program, which is already pretty well funded for several post-Apollo landing flights.

As a measure of its strong endorsement of unmanned application satellite programs, the NAS-NAE-NRC panel declared that in its view "the present space-applications program is too small by a factor of two or three, if we measure it in the light of the substantial opportunities that can be pursued effectively only if financial support is increased. Additional support would permit expansion of the applications program, and would enable the nation to proceed toward critically needed investments in preparation for future operation applications systems. NASA would be able to carry certain work through the space-flight operational experimental phase, so that both the potentials and the problems of future systems could be thoroughly understood."

MANNED FLIGHT

On the question of manned vs. unmanned flight, the panel noted: "We believe that the manned program has provided technological developments of importance to many aspects of space-flight and the use of space. It is expected that this will continue. In particular, the large booster program, tailored to the requirements of particular Earth orbits, will find applications in the orbiting of payloads for a variety of purposes. Additionally, this program will provide significant opportunities to test sensors and to prove out techniques useful to applications considered by this study. However, the use of manned vehicles per se does not at present appear necessary or economically desirable for the operation of the various space-applications systems considered by this study. We believe that the systems proposed for providing near-term practical and economic benefits to the U.S. public and to mankind generally will be achieved more effectively and economically with automated devices and vehicles. Manned programs must be justified in their own right; they cannot be justified in terms of space applications."

While it is true, especially in Washington, that distinguished panels come and go, and that more often than not, their recommendations are added to the already huge and dusty pile of reports and recommendations, never implemented, which by now must be as high as the Washington Monument, it seems clear that the philosophy of the NAS-NAE-NRC panel is in tune with the times. What the panel urged matches in tone and purpose the rising public and congressional pressure for more practical payoff from space and less emphasis on beating the Russians. This is not said to denigrate the achievement of Apollo but rather to reflect present political realities. While a great many Americans may stay up far into the night to monitor on television such an historic event as man's first walk on the moon, the enthusiasm needed to put up the monies to pay for continuous undertakings of this kind comes somewhat harder in a period plagued by inflation, war abroad, and frightening ferment at home.

DEMISE OF MOL

It was against this backdrop that the featured U.S. manned military space program, the Air Force's Manned Orbiting Laboratory (MOL) project, was shot down in June 1969. To the surprise of virtually everyone observing the space scene in the capital, the Nixon Administration suddenly cancelled MOL, declaring that the prime factors leading to the decision were "the continuing urgency of reducing federal defense spending and advances in automated techniques for unmanned satellite systems." Since MOL's initiation in the 1965, some $1.3 billion had been spent on the program when it was abruptly terminated. People close to the program say it will cost something like $100 million to close MOL out. There seems little doubt that the cancellation of MOL which, in the words of one high-placed Air Force space planner, puts the Air Force out of the manned space-flight business for the next eight or 10 years, represented a triumph of the Bureau of the Budget over the Defense Department in a season which has seen repeated attacks on military spending. The only remaining potential manned space-flight role for the Air Force would be as a partner with NASA in developing proposed Earth-to-orbit logistics vehicles. Both agencies have been directed to work together in this endeavor.

At the time of the MOL cancellation, there were suggestions in Washington that killing the jroject, for which the prime contractor was McDonnell-Douglas, was a gratuitous opportunity for the Nixon administration to strike a blow at Missouri's Democratic Senator Stuart Symington. Symington, a onetime Air Force Secretary and vociferous exponent of airpower, lately has been a loud critic of defense spending and an opponent of Safeguard ABM. Administration sources denied this suggestion, pointing out that although MOL contractor McDonnell-Douglas is headquartered in St. Louis, in Symington's home state, the major portion of the McDonnell-Douglas MOL work was in California. At any rate, the Senator complained loudly about the MOL cancellation.

MOL, which had been to the go-no-go brink all spring, had survived repeated examinations by the administration. Even as late as June 1, only a few days before its sudden demise, the highest echelons of the Air Force were sure the program would be continued, with manned launches expected in 1972. The likelihood is that MOL went down the drain as a kind of sacrifice—to demon strate that the Nixon Administration could find ways to cut back defense spending. Cynics added their suggestion at the time that the administration was doing a little trading for ABM votes too, which may or may not be true.

MOL VERSUS WORKSHOP

MOL's purpose had been to explore the military utility of man in space and to test an array of highly secret instruments. In many ways, MOL was similar to NASA's projected Orbital Workshop, a kind of manned testbed space station that would use an emptied-out S-4B Saturn booster stage to house astronauts for a period of up to 56 days and would serve as a predecessor to the large manned space station project NASA is studying and hoping to sell the administration on as the next big U.S. space program commitment. But, aside from hardware differences (MOL was to use Titan-3 boosters while Orbital Workshop is based on Apollo hardware) there were other important differences between the two projects. MOL was to have traveled in low polar orbits for obvious reconnaissance purposes while Workshop is designed for equatorial orbits flying higher paths.

Ironically, after MOL's cancellation, people in both NASA and the Air Force recalled that in 1968 there had been a close examination of both Orbital Workshop and MOL, in a cooperative study by both agencies. The 1968 conclusions were both technical and political. The political expectation then had been that if there had to be a choice on Capitol Hill between the two projects, MOL would survive because of its military significance. As to whether one of the projects could do the tasks of the other, it was determined that some of what NASA wanted to do aboard Workshop, physiological experiments and the like, could be done aboard MOL, but that conversely, very little of what the Air Force wanted to do aboard MOL could have been done aboard Workshop. The 1968 conclusions were rooted in the planned altitudes and polar orbits of the MOL.

WORKSHOP WINS

As matters turned out, it was MOL that died and Orbital Workshop that lived and it is the civilian space agency that is now examining MOL's carcass to see what might be salvaged. NASA is now looking at MOL's crew-feeding system, its waste-management hardware, the "articulated joint" pressure-suit designs, the environment controls for MOL's two-gas breathing system, and a few other items of MOL technology. But the bulk of MOL's onboard equipment that is salvageable will, according to Defense sources, go into classified military projects. So we shall never know how much of the more than $1 billion invested in MOL before its death will have been wasted.

How much of a loss to national security the demise of MOL occasions is a question hard to answer. To the more simple-minded critics of defense spending, killing the project must seem a cause for jubilation. It is probably true that most of essential observational tasks can be performed effectively in the unmanned mode. But there is little doubt that particular answers to the question of how man's presence might have enhanced the performance of those tasks will not be forthcoming to the degree of certitude the Air Force had in mind. Partial answers, at least by inference, to some of these questions can be gotten aboard vehicles such as NASA's Orbital Workshop, if the effort is made. But there is no assurance that NASA will make the effort. There are experts who believe that somehow it would have been wiser and more economical to have somehow effected a merger—despite the differences in planned missions and hardware—of Orbital Workshop and MOL.

NEW NASA ROLE?

In any case, there is a kind of object lesson for the Nixon Administration in the MOL affair. If the 1970s are to be a space decade heavily devoted to payoff and applications, then the kind of situation in which MOL and Workshop would compete, even in a general way and undeniably cost a great deal of money, should be averted in the future. This leads directly to the question of whether the role of NASA itself in the years ahead ought not to be re-examined quite closely. An important policy question that needs to be attacked is whether NASA in the 1970s should continue to be a huge operating agency. Are there ways to reorient NASA so that rather than being nearly a "fifth" service it would concentrate on producing, through research and development, new techniques and systems for turnover to user agencies whether military or civilian? For that matter, would it be possible to concentrate on using NASA's booster and other space hardware for the kinds of unmanned applications satellite programs advocated so vigorously in the NAS-NAE-NRC study alluded to above, rather than constantly searching for manned missions in Earth orbit or near and on the moon just for the sake of having manned missions?

Some would argue that such a policy would surrender control of space technology to the military or that NASA's vigor would be dissipated by a lessening of its considerable operational role. This need not be the case. The Defense Department and the whole range of other federal agencies with some interest in space have other things to worry about. And from a national point of view, unless there is a re-examination of the future role of NASA, we will face a continuing danger that the costs of a space program overly emphasizing manned exploration could swell out of proportion as time goes on, cancelling out the economic benefits that could accrue from a well-thought out and decently-funded applications program, unmanned, manned, or both. As a case in point, the military has had to develop expensive sites and buy costly hardware for its space programs during the same general period NASA has been doing much the same thing, also at huge cost. This is not to say that there has not been significant cooperation between the military and NASA in the execution of many important programs. There is in fact quite a complex network of cooperation and provision of services, one agency to another. But that network has taken years to build and has surely cost much more than it should have.

SPACE PRIORITIES

In the past decade of spectacular space achievements, the rush of events and the pressures of international competition flowing from national embarrassment have ruled policy. But a dozen years after Sputnik we should have enough wisdom and experience to chart a less costly course that would provide for a more careful distribution of space tasks among the various agencies of government and a greater standardization of boosters and other space hardware so that the maximum benefits can be extracted from space technology.

As the post-moon-landing decade opens, the President and his advisors simply cannot ignore the large body of opinion—public and congressional—that, for reasons ranging from worries about social problems at home to plain economy, takes exception to space spending in general. Once upon a time, such a dramatic demonstration of space prowess as the Soviet Soyuz rendezvous, docking and crew transfer, could have been counted on to bolster NASA budget requests. Today, Soviet accomplishments in space pass rapidly out of the headlines, and probably the only kind of Soviet achievement that would create really sharp public and congressional reaction would be an announced Soviet deployment of its weapon system in space.

Since it is Congress that is, presumably, responsive to public opinion, it would make sense for the pragmatic Mr. Nixon to take into account congressional expressions of priority in the space effort. Which takes the observer back to the calls for space payoff which are coming down from Capitol Hill.

One such recent demand issued from the House space committee's Subcommittee on Space Science and Applications, chaired by Rep. Joseph E. Karth, Democrat of Minnesota, one of the sharpest legislators on the House space panel. The subcommittee has issued a report sharply critical of NASA for what it considered NASA's foot-dragging of the Earth Resources Satellite system (ERS). The report said that "among those who have studied its implications there is virtual unanimity that an ERS system constitutes an idea whose time has come, and many believe that NASA's response is overdue." The report strongly recommended that NASA "concentrate a much larger portion of its efforts and resources on this project, and [that] the launch schedule should be compressed, if possible."

The ERS program, the report declared, ought to be unmanned and automated. The report went on to accuse NASA of submerging the ERS effort in the agency's enthusiasm for manned spaceflight. "The conclusion is inescapable," the report said, "that an automated ERS . . . project has been delayed because Earth resources experiments were, as a matter of NASA policy, [designed] to be carried out as part of the manned spaceflight program." Presumably such experiments have been viewed as a partial justification for the Apollo Applications program, and this may well have been the major obstacle to the exploitation of existing technology for development of an automated ERS spacecraft.

The Karth report warned too that with all due respect to the value of man in space, NASA's declining budgets may not permit many Apollo Applications manned flights in the 1970s and that a meaningful [unmanned] ERS program should not be required to wait upon such a contingent activity as Apollo Applications. The report added that "a truly productive ERS system will require much longer periods in orbit than are now contemplated for manned spaceflight," and that as NASA itself has acknowledged, "the orbital inclinations in manned flights are generally not considered ideal for ERS work."

All this is not so much an argument over unmanned vs. manned spaceflight, but rather a manifestation and recognition of the prime space-policy question of the 1970s: how the program of the future can best be devised so that the taxpayers who pick up the tab for space programs—no matter who runs which project—get their money's worth in terms of Earth-bound benefits.

PART III

THE FUTURE OF LUNAR STUDIES

HAROLD C. UREY

9. ORIGIN AND HISTORY OF THE MOON

Today, it is generally agreed that the great craters of the moon were produced by collisions of meteorite or asteroidal objects which arrived on the moon at some time during its long history. It is recognized also by all students of the subject that there has certainly been some volcanic history on the moon. Some prefer to believe that this consisted of great lava flows which filled the maria regions of the moon. Others doubt this, and suggest that there was some limited amount of water on the moon during its history, but admit that there are small crater-like volcanos on the moon which apparently were produced by some mild volcanic action. The problem of the origin of the moon is not understood at the present time, and we have no real consensus on the subject. However, for present purposes, we will assume that the moon had a low-temperature origin, that it has been at a moderate temperature through most of its history, that the great craters on its surface are indeed due to collisions and not to volcanic effects, and that there has been mild volcanic activity as indicated by certain small craters. The discussion will assume that the great maria are not due to the flow of lava. It is rather necessary to give an outline of conclusions, because the arguments are very much interrelated and all of them cannot be presented at any particular stage of the development of this discussion.

This article is based on a revision by the author and G. J. F. MacDonald of the author's chapter, "The Origin and History of the Moon" in Zdenek Kopal, ed., The Physics and Astronomy of the Moon (New York: Academic Press, 1962).

TIME OF SURFACE FORMATION

Collisions on the moon are so general that they can be assumed to have covered the entire surface of the moon. If such an intense collisional process had occurred on Earth, it would have destroyed all sedimentary and igneous rock formations up to the time of the collisions. These intense collisions, making craters of as much as 200 kilometers in diameter—even 500 kilometers in diameter and more if we consider the circular maria—must have shattered rocks to many kilometers below the surface of the moon. Hence, if the moon was bombarded intensely during any period of geologic time, the Earth must have been bombarded at the same time, and the entire geological record (prior to the time of bombardment) would have been destroyed. Since we have rocks on Earth that have been preserved for approximately three or 3.5 billion years, it is necessary to assume that the intense collisional processes on the moon occurred before that time. The meteorites indicate ages of 4.5 billion years, or perhaps even more, which means that these lunar collisions may have dated from the time of the formation of the solar system itself.

We now know, as a result of the studies of Ernest Opik and James Arnold, that objects such as meteorites cannot circulate in the neighborhood of the terrestrial planets for longer than perhaps tens of millions of years, indicating that the objects that hit the moon with this great intensity probably are part of the accumulation of the Earth and the planets generally, 4.5 billion years ago.

Indeed, this is an interesting possibility. It may be that the record we see on the moon indicates the method of terrestrial origin, namely the accumulation from solid objects some 4.5 billion years ago—a conclusion which was first suggested some 20 years ago and is widely accepted today. Of course, such an origin suggests that the surface of the moon may have been bombarded with material of mean Earth composition, but if this is the case, the surface of the moon for some unknown thickness should be covered with approximately meteoritic material. This is not confirmed by the experiments of

Anthony Turkevich and his colleagues who studied the scattering of alpha particles from the material of the moon. The conclusion that one can come to as a result of this is that the surface layer of collisions of terrestrial type must be a thin one. No metal has been observed on the surface of the moon by the latest experiments; for some reason any metallic content has been displaced below the surface.

One of the objectives in bringing materials back from the surface of the moon is to attempt to determine what the age of the surface of the moon may be. The potassium-argon ages and the uranium-thorium-helium ages will probably not be very reliable because of degassing by collisions, but we should be able to get good results from rubidium-strontium and the lead-lead ages. It may be difficult to distinguish the results of such determinations from what might be expected if the collisions that fashioned the surface of the moon have been occurring all through geologic time.

The circular maria are undoubtedly due to such collisions, and it would appear, as I have maintained for 20 years, that the large objects which produced maria and the smaller ones which produced the craters were all part of one single bombardment event—first a mare, then many minor collisions, then another mare, etc.— so that the surface of the moon should be covered with buried maria. Finally, the whole process stopped, leaving buried maria as well as fresh smooth ones such as Imbrium. Since then, the moon has been bombarded by the occasional meteoritic type of object coming at high velocity and forming the ray craters and many smaller ones. It is probable that the collisional process, for the most part, occurred early in the history of the moon, and that the objects that fell on its surface were moving in orbits in the neighborhood of the Earth-moon system, finally arriving at comparatively low velocities, probably at the escape velocity of the moon or somewhat larger.

TEMPERATURE HISTORY

It has been known for many years that the dynamical characteristics of the moon's orbit and its libration in longitude and latitude indicate that the moon has a tri-axial ellipsoidal shape, the three moments of inertia being different from those expected under the gravitational forces of the moon and Earth. This conclusion rests upon well established data, and has been known for many years. Sir Harold Jeffreys noted that these data indicate a stress at the center of the moon of as much as 19 bars (one bar equals about 0.98697 standard atmosphere pressure). It is surprising indeed that an object the size of the moon should maintain such a stress for this long period of time.

Some years ago, Professor Walter M. Elsasser, George D. Rochester and I suggested that perhaps there is a variation of density with angle on the moon, producing differences in the moments of inertia which are seen in astronomical observations. This would explain the irregular shape of the moon. The phenomenon might result from collisions of objects of varying density; we estimated that the number might be as high as 29,000, with masses in the neighborhood of 10^{21} grams. The variation of moments of inertia might be due to a few large objects of varying density, rather than to many as we have suggested.

This evidence has been with us for many years, and has been discussed many times in the astronomical literature. In spite of this, many assumptions have been made indicating a very high temperature for the lunar interior without any attempt at all to account for these physical facts which rest upon well established astronomical theory.

GRAVITATIONAL FIELD

The orbiters have given us much information about the gravitational field of the moon. Extensive studies of this kind have been made at the Jet Propulsion Laboratory (JPL) and at Goddard Space Flight Center, and it turns out that the gravitational shape of the moon is even more complicated than would be indicated by its simple tri-axial ellipsoidal shape.

The expansion of the gravitational field in terms of

Legendre polynomials describing the ellipsoidal shape would require that the coefficients which are designated as $C_{2,0}$ and $C_{2,2}$ should be a finite size and that higher terms should be small or not present at all. It is found that the higher terms are present, and this indicates that no simple tri-axial ellipsoidal shape can possibly explain the results. Also, these irregularities indicate that there are stress differences in the interior of the moon from the order of magnitude of some 40 or 50 bars near the surface to smaller values in the deeper interior. However, even after analyzing the moon out to Legendre polynomials of tenth order, an exact description of the surface is not acquired. When all of these things are taken into account, there are residues from the calculations which exceed the observational errors. These errors are remarkably small—about one-hundredth of a centimeter per second squared (0.1 cm/sec^2) in the acceleration.

P. M. Muller and W. L. Sjogren of JPL had the brilliant idea of using the Lunar Orbiters as direct accelerometers. As a result, they have been able to show that there are increased attractive masses below certain areas on the front side of the moon—the largest being over Mare Imbrium and Mare Serenitatis, and the smaller ones in other locations over the circular mare and a few other places not previously recognized as maria areas.

These measurements indicate that there are mass concentrations below the surface of the moon which have been called mascons. William M. Kaula has used Gauss's theorem in order to determine the excess mass located in these positions. This is the best calculation of this quantity that has been made to date. I, myself, used a flat slab with the diameter of the mare, and others have attempted to explain it as due to water sediments and as due to lava flows.

What is immediately evident is that gravitational isostacy has not occurred on the surface of the moon, and this, I think, rules out completely all possibility of explaining these objects by lava flows. Gravitational anomalies on Earth result from lava flows, but these are usually in high mountain areas, or places where we believe that convection currents in the mantle produced low gravitational anomalies in the neighboring land. An example is the shores of the Pacific and the trenches before these areas. The mascons on the moon are in relatively low areas—in the maria which are possibly somewhat lower than the mountainous areas. But there appears to be no similarity to the areas of high and low gravitational anomalies that we see on Earth. Incidentally, Sinus Iridum is the only low gravitational anomaly on the moon, and is substantial in size.

The masses which must be attributed to the mascons are approximately those for the objects which collided with the moon, as indicated by the estimated energies required to produce the maria and using the escape velocity of the moon as a possible velocity of these objects. The difficulties with this theory are that many people prefer to believe that the maria were created by impacts of high velocity objects which scattered material over great distances. Personally, I find little evidence for enormous scattering of material on the moon's surface, amounting to say millions of cubic kilometers of material. Moreover, I believe that it is entirely reasonable to believe that the objects that form the primitive craters and maria arrived at about the escape velocity of the moon. They were moving in the neighborhood of the Earth-moon orbit when they were captured, or they were indeed satellites of Earth, and collided in a very short period of time with the surface of the moon. I am assuming that the velocities of the colliding objects were so low that their energy was only sufficient to melt the object itself and some of the neighboring material.

Regardless of what we believe the origin of these objects may be, it appears that the moon could not have been at high temperature at any time after these mascons were established on the surface of the moon. Moreover, the shape of the moon could not have been produced by tidal effects combined with the rotation of the moon on its axis. This is a most important conclusion for the question of the origin of the moon. It will be interesting to see whether we can find any evidence for it as a result of the Apollo landings.

COMPOSITION OF THE MOON

If the moon escaped from the Earth, as was suggested by Sir George Darwin, its composition is quite easily explained, since it is the same as the mantle of the Earth. The difficulty with this hypothesis is that no one has yet come up with an acceptable theory of the moon's escape, either as a single body or as individual particles. It appears that if either of these methods of escape occurred, then the moon would have formed in the plane of the equator of the Earth. But studies, particularly those by Peter Goldreich, indicate that the moon could never have been in the equatorial plane of the Earth.

The composition of the moon is also very much in agreement with the non-volatile fraction of the sun, as has been reported over the last 15 years. Curiously, the amount of iron in the sun has been reported to be less than that of the meteorites and less than that of the Earth by about a factor of five. At present, there is some indication that this figure may be wrong. There is a group of people who think that iron must be more abundant. It should be noted that Mercury undoubtedly has a density indicating the presence of about 60 or 65 per cent of metallic iron, and the moon has distinctly less iron than the Earth, perhaps only 10 per cent. Mars has perhaps 20 per cent of iron in it, judging from its density, and Venus and Earth should have perhaps 30 or more per cent of iron in their makeup. Thus there has been an enormous fractionation of iron in the solar system.

LUNAR HEAT BALANCE

I have suggested an origin of the moon which is consistent with a composition similar to that of the sun. This idea goes back nearly 15 years and I have not seen any reason to abandon it. It is possible to use the composition of the Earth with respect to iron and assume that the moon contains increased amounts of water. This immediately raises the problem of how the moon acquired large amounts of water—and the Earth so little. It also raises the question of whether melting within the interior of the moon would not be more probable than is indicated by the irregular shape and the existence of the mascons.

The fact that the moon has mascons and an irregular shape indicates that it must have been rigid throughout its history. This narrows the problem of its heat balance. The moon could not have been formed in a molten state —otherwise the mascons would not have been supported, at least during the early history of the moon. It therefore must have been made at low temperatures. But even if the moon had been made at a temperature of $0°C$ (the approximate temperature at this distance from the sun at the present time) its potassium, uranium and thorium content would be equal to that of the most abundant types of chondritic meteorites, the L and H type meteorites. In that case, the temperature of the moon would have become impossibly high at the present time. This is shown by all the calculations that have been made by all students of the subject. It therefore seems necessary to consider the possibility that the radioactive elements in some way are less abundant in the moon than in these more abundant types of meteorites.

Some years ago Gerald Wasserburg, Gordon MacDonald, William Fowler and Fred Hoyle pointed out that the potassium-uranium ratio in surface rocks of the Earth was about 10^4 to one, whereas it is about six or eight times that in the meteorites, and they suggested that for some reason or other the Earth did not have as much potassium relative to uranium and thorium as is present in the meteorites. The abundances in the meteorites change slightly with time. The carbonaceous chondrites Type III have about 350 or 360 parts per million of potassium—considerably less than in other meteorites. If we use this abundance and assume that this applies to the moon, it is possible to start with a low-temperature moon and find that it does not get to melting temperatures at the present time. The average temperature would be some 700 or 800 degrees, which would be in accord with the conductivity of the moon, as indicated by the flow of the solar wind and its magnetic lines of force past the surface of the moon. This is a point that has been established by Norman Ness, especially, as a result of the study of Lunar Orbiter 35.

POTASSIUM UNCERTAINTY

The abundance of potassium in the sun has been an uncertain figure. Recent data indicate about 3,200 atomic parts of potassium relative to one million of silicon. But in the past, Laurence Aller and some others have secured values running to about half that, and this would agree with the abundance in the Type III carbonaceous chondrites. If we ues this abundance, it is possible that the moon can remain at low temperatures, and thus we may account for a rigid and cold moon. It is difficult to see how potassium became fractionated in the numerous types of chondrites, but these bodies are not the average solar composition with respect to many elements, in addition to iron. The Type I carbonaceous chondrite of which we have a few samples (one, the Orgueil meteorite, has been analyzed in detail) would have a potassium abundance that varies somewhat on the basis of different analyses. But it has an abundance of potassium indicated at 3,500 or 3,800, and hence its abundance of potassium would be a less desirable choice for the moon. Some of our colleagues have made extensive studies of possible differentiation of the moon with radioactive elements concentrated in the surface regions, but these studies suggest extensive lava flows over the entire surface of the moon some one or two billion years ago. This would mean that the intense collisional history must have occurred since that time, which appears to be impossible because the geologic evidence indicates that there has been no such history of the Earth since about 3.5 aeons ago.

SURFACE COMPOSITION

The Turkevich analyses indicate that the surface of the moon has approximately the composition of basalt. Two analyses, in Tranquillitatis and the center of the disk of the moon, agree with respect to all the elements very well. The anlysis, at a point near Tycho, indicates very similar composition, except for less iron. This difference in iron content makes it more difficult to understand the composition of the moon. The experiments of de Wys indicate that there is very little metallic iron in the surface of the moon. The Russian analyses indicate that the potassium content is within the lower range of basalt; it is, I think, quite impossible to conclude definitely whether this is the same as that of the chondrites or a few times that concentration. The potassium content in the basalt on Earth often runs as high as one or two per cent. This is a relatively high concentration of potassium, so that terrestrial basalt must come from the interior of the Earth.

If the abundance of an element is increased by a factor of 20 over the primordial abundance, it must be derived from 20 times the amount of material in which the primordial abundance is found. This means that terrestrial basalt has been formed from a large fraction of interior rocks. If we find that the concentration of basalt on the surface of the moon is high, then it will be necessary to assume that the basalt has been extracted from a large fraction of material of the moon, and this will present serious problems in explaining such differentiation. On the other hand, if the basalt is relatively low in potassium, then I think it is possible to account for this material by assuming that a layer on the outer part of the moon has been melted and allowed to crystallize slowly. In that case, the residual surface material would have a composition of basalt, and the first material at somewhat deeper layers is probably that of the enstatite or other achondrites. This will be an important question to be decided by the Apollo 11 flight and will make a definite contribution to limitations that must be met in accounting for the origin and history of the moon. It would be interesting to learn whether magnetic materials, i.e., nickel-iron, exist in the regions of the mascons.

WATER ON THE MOON

Quite a number of people have suggested that there has been water on the moon. I suggested this many years ago, but have not followed it up very vigorously. John J. Gilvarry has insisted that there was an enormous amount of water on the moon for a long period of time. Z. Kopal and Thomas Gold suggest that there is water beneath the surface of the moon, but do not like the idea of surface water. In recent years, astronomers Donald Menzel and Barbara Middlehurst have pointed out features that look as though they were shaped by water, and recently Sjogren and Muller have come to this same conclusion. The idea that there has been water on the moon has been growing steadily over the last 10 years. It is surprising that geologists have been so thoroughly tied to the basalt idea, yet have not been willing to consider in a friendly way the possibility of a sedimentary type of development for the smooth areas of the moon. The mascon with a negative anomaly in Sinus Iridum is very difficult to understand, unless the object that produced Mare Imbrium ploughed in through Sinus Iridum and left a cavity which was filled with low density material. What comes to mind is sedimentary rock, perhaps mixed with water or something of that sort.

There are many features of the surface of the moon that are very difficult to explain in terms of the lava hypothesis. This was pointed out many years ago by Thomas Gold, who remarked that it is difficult to believe that lava tubes coming from deep inside the moon have flowed up into all the little crevices and craters of many parts of the moon to produce this nice smooth layer. As a matter of fact, many of them are of approximately the same level, and it looks very much as though water could have seeped through the fragmented surface, establishing an equi-potential surface early in the history of the moon. It is my belief that water was briefly present as a surface material on the moon in its very early history. I object to the assumption that water was present for a long time because I find little evidence for valleys of the type that we see on Earth, where water washes mountains down into the sea in about 20 million years.

I cannot but believe that if water had been on the moon for long periods of time, all the mountains of the moon would have been smoothed out, including those on the far side.

Since I believe that there is no evidence for extensive folded mountains on the moon of the type found on Earth, I think the moon would have been completely smooth if this had been the case. Limited water for a limited period of time is to my mind indicated by the pictures of the moon. It will be interesting to see whether Apollo brought back hydrated minerals or pseudomorphs of hydrated minerals at least of microscopic size. Unfortunately, the surface regions of the moon have been bombarded, disturbed and dehydrated to a very large degree, especially in the equatorial regions, and we may not be able to see these effects very clearly. It is my hope that we will be able to find small crystals that will answer this question.

THE MOON AS A PLANET

It has been my belief that the moon is an ancient object, probably captured by Earth at the beginning of terrestrial history. If this is the case, it must have been made somewhere, independent of the Earth, and would therefore be an independent planet and an exceedingly interesting object. Stepping on the moon would have the same interest as stepping on Mars, or the asteroids or Venus.

There are certain things that support this point of view. I thought this 20 years ago when I began to study the moon, and I think so today.

The data that we have presented here indicate that the moon was formed at a low temperature—it was not melted or even warm in its early history—and that it is not exceedingly hot today. This is based upon the presence of the mascons which were probably produced 4.5 billion years ago and have remained in position throughout the entire history of the moon. This means that for some hundreds of kilometers the moon must be sufficiently rigid to support very high stresses. The irregular shape of the moon suggests this same conclusion.

ACCUMULATING DEBRIS

One may ask how the Earth and terrestrial planets accumulated. Some years ago, Gerard P. Kuiper suggested that proto-planets of great mass, equal to the mass of the planets plus the solar component of gas, were formed by gravitational instability. I objected to this, for I did not see how it was possible to explain the loss of enormous masses of the heavier gases (for example, xenon) which could be expected to be present on Earth in substantial amounts unless we devised some exceedingly effective way to remove them. We must assume exceedingly violent processes in the early history of the solar system if this is not the case. It seems to me that the most reasonable assumption is that the gases were lost before objects the size of the Earth and other terrestrial planets were accumulated. In this case, the gas was blown out and the planets accumulated from solid objects such as we see, for example, on the surface of the moon.

There is a problem relating to the way in which solid objects such as the Earth can accumulate from small fractured debris. The asteroids are presently disintegrating due to collisions, and I see no reason why asteroidal-sized objects in the past would not have disintegrated in this same way. However, if we had a solar nebula consisting of asteroidal objects, and we tossed in a few lunar-sized objects, the planets would accumulate without any trouble at all. The lunar-sized objects colliding with objects moving at only escape velocity, or essentially escape velocity, would grow in size and sweep up all the materials within certain regions in their neighborhood. Probably two lunar-sized objects would collide to give a fairly large mass, which would begin the sweep-up process of many objects. It seems that gases are necessary to dissipate the energy of collisions and produce objects the size of the Earth or the moon.

Probably Jupiter is one that accumulated because of the presence of gases, but the Earth must have accumulated in the absence of gases.

I suggested quite a number of years ago that gravitational instability should have produced lunar-sized objects. This suggestion resulted from a study of Kuiper's ideas of how the protoplanets formed. I maintained that we must have smaller objects, but having found a way to accumulate solid objects to lunar-sized objects, I then found that I had accumulated the moon without intending to do so. In addition to the difficulty of accumulating solids into large bodies such as the Earth, starting with small materials, there is the difficulty of accounting for the inclined axis of the Earth and Mars. The rotation of Venus and Mercury has probably been thoroughly disturbed by tidal effects from the sun. If the Earth and Mars accumulated out of small-sized objects, the mean angular momentum axis should have been perpendicular to the plane of the ecliptic, and no inclined axis of the Earth and Mars should result. It would appear that these inclined axes are due to accumulation from substantial-sized objects, which would have a relative angular momentum to the accumulating Earth or other planets different from the perpendicular to the plane of the ecliptic. Thus, it would seem that there are good reasons for believing that the accumulation of planets involved a coalition of some objects larger than the asteroidal type that we see now.

The moon may be one of many such objects. It is quite certain that if one tossed a moon into the neighborhood of the terrestrial planets at the present time, it would be exceedingly probable that within a few tens of millions of years it would collide with one of these objects and coalesce with them. It would be a most unusual thing if it should be captured into nearly circular orbits such as the moon is moving in at the present time. If we had many objects like the moon moving in the neighborhood of the sun, it is entirely possible that one of these might have been captured by one of the terrestrial planets as observed. This would substantially decrease the improbability of the event. Moreover, if the capture occurred during the terminal stage of the accumulation of the Earth, we could expect that there would be objects present with which the moon could collide, and hence dissipate some of the energy of capture in this way. Also, if there were satellites of the Earth smaller than the moon at that time, the moon could throw some of these objects off the Earth-moon system into space and lose energy in this way. It is necessary to assume, if the moon was captured, that it was not heated by tidal friction or something of that sort. The mascons indicate that the moon was cold at the beginning and has remained that way ever since. For that reason, we must, if we have a captured moon, account for the dissipation of energy in other ways.

LUNAR LANDING

It should be noted that if there were many moons around in the early history of the solar system, they would not be there today, for by this time they would have collided with each other, or with the present planets, and would have disappeared completely. It also may be true that if there had been a moon in the neighborhood of the asteroidal areas, these objects would not exist. There is some indication that the accumulation process died off as the major planets were approached. A different type of accumulation took place in the outer part of the solar system—possibly resulting from the presence of smaller objects than those in the terrestrial region, which retained their gas at the time the accumulation process was taking place—thus producing planets which have considerable amounts of gas attached to them.

If this is the true origin of the terrestrial planets, the moon can be regarded as a part of the evolution of the solar system, not as an incidental object that escaped from an insignificant planet Earth to produce an insignificant chip. It would be part of the evolution of stars into planetary systems, and thus part of the processes that are taking place throughout the cosmos. I admit to being prejudiced. I had hoped that the moon would be an interesting subject. If I had not felt that it was an object of this kind, here is one scientist that would have never spent any time on studying the moon at all. I am not interested in having an object repeat the geological history of the Earth. Geology can be studied much more interestingly on the Earth than it can possibly be studied on the moon. The expense of exploring the moon to the degree with which the Earth can be explored would, in my opinion, not be worth the effort at all. But if the moon is this fundamental object that accumulated early in the history of the solar system, then it is worth it, and I hope that the Apollo flights will prove that this is the case.

IRVING MICHELSON

10. A SPACE AGE PHENOMENON: THE EVOLUTION OF LUNAR STUDIES

The origin and evolution of the solar system is ranked first in the National Academy of Sciences current listing of the central scientific problems of our time. A detailed knowledge of the structure and composition of the moon would be of inestimable value in resolving this age-old problem. The question has become susceptible to scientific analysis on the basis of quantitative physical data only within the past decade, although the lunar sciences are still necessarily permeated by sheer speculation to a large degree.

American and Soviet space programs have provided instruments and vehicles capable of transmitting to the earth the data on which a proper physical science can be based. Ranger, Orbiter, Surveyor and Luna spacecraft findings, so essential for near-term planning of manned missions, are also of immense significance in the long-range studies of cosmogony, the physical theory of the creation of the world. Certain judgments can now be made concerning the intrinsic scientific value of contemporary space technology.

THE BASIC CONSTANTS

Before the advent of space flight, lunar studies were so severely handicapped that E. W. Brown, the foremost authority on lunar theory, was obliged to conclude that even such a basic quantity as the total mass of the moon might never be evaluated with an accuracy better than five per cent of its true value. With regard to lunar structure, or the distribution of mass within the moon, so little is known that inferences drawn in different ways are flatly contradictory to each other. Although the total lunar mass is now believed to be determined with an acceptable accuracy, the same is by no means true of the principal inertia moments that characterize the internal mass distribution in gross form, still less of the lunar gravity harmonics that could specify the structure completely. Inertia moments determine the characteristics of the rotational motion of any rigid body, and it is a curious fact that although the moon's rotational motion has been very accurately known for nearly three centuries, attempts to infer values of the inertia moments have been notoriously unsuccessful.

Astronomers have traditionally pointed to the determination of the lunar mass as one of the most perplexing and arduous tasks in the history of their science, but the inertia moments that are even more precious from the standpoint of cosmogony have remained still more obscure. Specifically, the dimensionless differences formed by the three principal inertia moments are sought as keys to the origin and evolution enigma, and they are scarcely better known now than in the time of the Marquis de Laplace, French astronomer and mathematician, nearly 200 years ago. Upper bounds for these differences are still being revised from year to year by different workers, the values given by one authority rarely agreeing with those of any other. Traditionally the basis for all estimates of inertia moment differences was telescopic observation of the irregularities of lunar rotation, and these have been too small to measure with any degree of confidence.

"PHYSICAL LIBRATIONS"

More than 200 years ago, in 1764, the French Academy of Sciences set as the topic of its coveted annual prize essay the problem of the rotation of the moon, from which the inertia moments might be deduced. The leading mathematicians of Europe entered the competition, and the prize was awarded to J. L. Lagrange, the French geometer and astronomer. The prize-winning essay bears little resemblance to his later and more famous work that was taken over and incorporated into Laplace's celebrated treatise, and is chiefly important for initiating a long-enduring interest in the problem on the part of both of these great mathematicians. For the next 60 years, both Lagrange and Laplace studied the "physical librations," as Galileo termed the nonuniformities of the lunar rotational motion, and Lagrange's calculation of 1780 as it appears anonymously in Laplace's *Traité de Mécanique Céleste*, published in 1798, remains to this day the standard development of the question.

Lagrange's efforts on this problem, it might be noted, were so taxing of his energies that he believed that his health was permanently impaired by the ordeal. It was on this account that he undertook a scientific study to determine the number of hours each day that he might work without further injury to his frail constitution, and thereafter scrupulously avoided exceeding the limit he set for himself. To understand the fervor of Lagrange in his labors on the physical librations, it is necessary to recall a startling discovery concerning the lunar librations which was seen as a threat to the very foundations of classical mechanics, that is, to Newton's laws of motion themselves.

CASSINI AND HIS "LAWS"

Primitive telescopic observations conducted by J. D. Cassini, a French hydraulic engineer-turned-astronomer, led him to discover in 1693 (seven years after the appearance of Newton's *Principia* and its laws of motion) that the rotation of the moon is described with very great accuracy by three distinct statements. These three of "Cassini's laws," as they were termed, if strictly and accurately true, cannot be reconciled with Newton's laws of motion. Cassini's empirical findings assert that: (1) the moon rotates at a uniform rate of speed so as to display toward the earth always the same portion of its surface; (2) the axis of lunar rotation forms a small and constant angle with the normal to the ecliptic plane; and (3) the descending node of the lunar equator on the ecliptic plane coincides always and exactly with the ascending node of the plane of the moon's orbit.

The difficulty raised by these exquisitely simple "laws" is in their claim to perfect precision. For there are always small gravitational forces acting on the moon (by virtue of Newton's law of gravitation), and the laws of motion require these to be accompanied by accelerations that manifest themselves as irregularities of rotational motion. These irregularities might be, and in fact certainly are, very small—but unless they are positively identified, Newton's laws of motion would appear to be violated once, and for evermore suspect. The grim fact is that standard optical and photographic methods have never yet clearly established the existence of the physical librations. If the irregular angular displacements are as small as a few minutes of arc measured from the moon's center, as presently supposed, uncertainties of measurement prevent collection of meaningful quantitative data by standard Earth-based means.

The most illustrious of the world's scientific thinkers have recognized the importance of a knowledge of the moon's structure and rotational characteristics as a clue to the history of the only solitary planetary satellite in the solar system. (All other planets have either no satellites or multiple ones.) The temptation to regard the moon as part of a double planet system is great, but there is also insufficient knowledge on which to base such a unique classification. Johannes Kepler, Galileo and Newton in the seventeenth "century of genius" all displayed an interest in the lunar rotation prior to Cassini's discovery and the subsequent theoretical investigations of Jean Le Rond d'Alembert, French mathematician and philosopher, Lagrange and Laplace. Each of these giants of intellect seems to have been aware of the inadequacy of his own findings. The theory of the moon's physical librations stands today in essentially the same form as Laplace left it 150 years ago—mostly an enigma.

NEBULA HYPOTHESIS

Laplace's special concern with physical librations was related to his cosmogonic studies, much the same as now, and played a role in his adoption of the solar nebula hypothesis known by the names Kant-Laplace. Specifically, he sought an answer to the question whether the moon might have been fluid just prior to assuming its present form. Detailed calculations he had made for the gravitational potential of liquid ellipsoids furnished values of eccentricity (and hence the principal inertia moments) that he attempted to confirm by means of the librations analysis. The scanty data available to him led to his assignment of upper bounds for the inertia moment differences so much greater than the potential calculations had indicated that he thereupon rejected the possibility of a primeval liquid moon. In the light of present suppositions concerning the smallness of physical librations, there is some doubt whether Laplace was correct in recognizing a discrepancy between the potential and librations calculations—and hence in deciding against the "big bang" hypothesis that was being strongly urged by his elder contemporary, Georges Buffon. The prolific and imaginative Buffon, a man of all sciences, held that a giant comet had once collided with the sun, causing fragments to break off which subsequently collapsed and formed the entire solar system.

As long as cosmogony was a gentleman's game of witty and subtle speculations, secure against the intrusion of new physical evidence, Laplace was free to modify Immanuel Kant's hypothesis in a small but essential detail before claiming it for his own. In the final note of Laplace's *Système du Monde*, the Kant-Laplace theory envisions an immense primeval dust cloud rotating around the sun. (Kant himself assumed the cloud to be initially at rest, in a manner that ignored the principle of conservation of angular momentum.)

Virtually all hypotheses of lunar origin fall into one or the other of these two classes of ideas proposed by Buffon and Kant-Laplace. The nebula hypothesis generally was favored until the beginning of this century, when variations of the catastrophic models gained the ascendancy. These have in turn been displaced in modern times by newly modified versions of the gradual evolution concept of Kant-Laplace, the earlier objections to which have been met in large measure by modern conceptions of turbulence presented by von Weizsäcker and Ter Haar. The question is still largely one of personal taste, however, whether to adopt one viewpoint or the other. As Harold C. Urey has said, "All explanations for the origin of the moon are improbable."

COSMOGONIC CONFUSION

What has made it impossible to decide rationally among the possible lunar histories that have been proposed is the gross insufficiency of available data. Much more knowledge about the moon's physical state is needed than was available at the beginning of this decade, for example, in order to reject fallacious hypotheses.

Because the average density of the moon is roughly equal to that of the earth's mantle, but considerably less than the earth's average density, there are grounds to accept the belief that the moon was torn away from the earth by some catastrophic event. This notion conforms with Buffon's eighteenth century ideas and those of Sir James Jeans and Sir Harold Jeffreys in our own times. It has been commonly supposed, moreover, that the moon is nearly homogeneous (uniform density throughout) and of chemical composition similar to terrestrial silicate phases of chondrites.

A quite different picture emerges from studies of the translational motion of the moon (i.e., the motion of its center of mass) around the Earth and, together with the Earth, around the sun. The periodic motions of the lunar orbital node (18.6 year period) and perigee (8.85 year period) are known with great precision by observation, resulting from the combined effects of hundreds of separate physical causes. One of the least well known of these is the non-uniformity of the internal mass dis-

tribution within the moon. This provides a basis for esti-
mating lunar inertia moment differences, if other factors
are considered to be well evaluated. The inference is
then drawn that one of the inertia moment differences
is much larger than other theories would permit, implying that the densest regions of the moon are nearest to
its surface, in what has been termed the "hollow moon"
hypothesis. The apparent density inversion needed to
provide consistency in the theory of the moon's orbital
motion, termed the lunar theory, is not only unfamiliar
but wholly unacceptable on a physical-mechanical basis
—a hollow shell of this type would necessarily collapse.

MASCON MYSTERY

Neither the supposition of a nearly uniform lunar
structure nor the "hollow moon" theory can be verified
by the traditional librations studies. It is even questionable whether perfectly accurate data on librations and
inertia differences, when these do become available, will
provide sufficiently fine detail to permit definite conclusions. The different harmonics of the moon's gravity
field, when accurately determined, on the other hand,
represent a more complete description of the internal
mass distribution so vital in devising a plausible lunar
history.

There was, however, no way of determining this information until U.S. Lunar Orbiter and Russian Luna
spacecraft were sent into orbit around the moon in the
last two years. Lunar Orbiter 5, in particular, circuiting
the moon once every three hours and 11 minutes over a
10-day period displayed unexpected orbital characteristics that have led to a most important discovery. Data
received at the Deep Space Network tracking system on
the Earth revealed the presence of a strong but initially
unidentified influence that modified the observed orbit
to an appreciable degree. A new analysis of the orbital
data reported by P. M. Muller and W. L. Sjogren of the
Jet Propulsion Laboratory has revealed strong gravitational anomalies in much the same manner that a sensi-

tive mine detector locates its concealed prey. It has become clear that very large concentrations of mass (now termed mascons) are situated at no fewer than seven sites on the lunar nearside. When the spacecraft passed close to these buried masses, the resultant lunar gravitational attraction it experienced was abruptly and drastically modified, thereby changing the subsequent path in much the same manner as if engine thrust had been applied.

The gravitational variations caused by the mascons amounts to about one per cent of total lunar gravity. This suggests that individual mascons may represent as much as 1/50,000 of the moon's total mass. The full extent of the mascons has yet to be determined.

Nevertheless, the existence of the mascons can be summoned to support several hypotheses, including Laplace's conviction that the moon did not solidify from a liquid state, as well as the theory that the moon was subject to severe bombardment by huge meteorites that may be identified with the mascons. Cassini's assertion of the perfect uniformity of the moon's rotational motion might also be explained by the mascons, since their effect would be to contribute to a lunar structure particularly conducive to the extremely stable motion that the observed regularity represents. Newtonian mechanics and gravitation certainly also stand firm in this new picture, and the formerly inexplicably high values of the largest inertia moment difference can likewise be fully accounted for by the presence of the mascons.

Looking ahead, it is appropriate to seek implications in various disciplines. With regard to future lunar explorations, and especially for further manned landings, precision orbit control will require determination of the influence of all mascons collectively and also individually on the motion of the spacecraft in the vicinity of the moon.

In the lunar sciences per se, the evidence of non-isostatic conditions prevailing in the moon's interior requires attention to the stress stage and composition of the interior. The manner in which the mascons accumulated, very possibly by violent impact, must be studied as one vital factor in any formation hypothesis relating to the origin of the solar system.

It now is possible to investigate these long standing problems of lunar structure, with their implications in the origin and evolution of the Earth, the moon and the solar system, from a new base of operations—the moon itself.

JOHN A. O'KEEFE

11. MANNED LANDINGS AND THEORIES OF LUNAR FORMATION

There is an ancient Irish folk-tale, rewritten by Padraic Colum in a book called *The King of Ireland's Son*, about a prince who goes out into the world to find the secret of his own childhood—the beginning and the end of the Unique Tale. His companion on the quest is Gilly of the Goatskin; and in the end, it appears that the boyhood of neither can be understood without the other.

In the history of the Earth, there is a blank period. From the study of meteorites, it has become clear that the date of formation of the solar system is about —4.7 billion years. There is also evidence from the lead isotopes of the Earth that it was formed at about the same time. But the earliest rocks have dates on the order of —3.5 billion years. What was happening during that first billion years of the Earth's history?

It won't do to say that the Earth was just cooling down. If the Earth ever was hot, which some people doubt, the time required to form a solid crust was of the order of a few thousand years, as Sir Harold Jeffreys has calculated. It probably wasn't any remarkable activity of the sun; since meteorites are much more fragile than the Earth, they would have been destroyed by any terrible solar eruption—for example, the sun becoming a nova. It appears that there was some local catastrophe.

Preston Cloud has brought forward evidence that this catastrophe involved the moon. He finds evidence that as we go back in time, the tides were greater than they are now, as though the moon had been closer. And in fact, there is abundant evidence, both geological and astronomical that, a few billion years back, the moon was closer to the Earth.

Traditionally, there have been three theories of the origin of the moon: that it was formed alongside the Earth, at the time when the Earth formed; that it was formed out in space, and was captured by the Earth; and that it was formed by the breakup of the Earth. Of these theories, the first is probably wrong if the event of −3.5 billion years had anything to do with the moon. Once the moon was formed, in whatever manner, near the Earth, both theory and observation show that it will move steadily outward as a result of tidal friction. This transfers the energy of the Earth's rotation to the moon's orbital velocity. The process is like the way you get a stone on the end of a rope to swing around. You put your hand above your head, and make it go around in a small circle. Soon the stone is going around in a much larger circle. Here the motion of your hand, in the small circle, is the rotation of the Earth; the string represents the attraction of the Earth's tidal bulge on the moon; and the stone represents the moon. The tidal bulge is the whole mass of water which has been raised up by the moon's attraction; it also includes a significant component from the deformation of the solid Earth itself.

LANDINGS MAY DECIDE

Theory indicates that the effect of tidal friction will vary with the inverse sixth power of the distance from the moon to the Earth. Hence the moon must have re-ceded rapidly from the Earth until it was, say, half its present distance. It is thus impossible that the moon could have been formed along with the Earth at −4.7 billion years, and then remained in its neighborhood for a billion years. It would, so far as we can now see, have gone out to something like its present distance by −3.5 billion years.

It seems likely that the manned lunar landings will yield information enabling investigators to decide be-tween the other two theories, namely the theory of rotational breakup of the Earth and the capture theory. It seems likely that the trace element abundances in the returned sample will be measurably different depending on which theory is correct. This is particularly true for the noble elements: gold, platinum, nickel, osmium, iridium, palladium, rhodium, ruthenium, molybdenum and others.

The reference level for abundance measurements is a standard scheme of relative abundances, which is called the system of cosmic abundances. This scheme represents the original abundance ratios in which the elements of the solar system were formed. Although there is considerable doubt about the precise manner in which the elements were formed, there is comparatively little doubt about the relative abundance ratios at that time. One gets approximately the same answer when the proper allowances are made, whether one starts from the atmosphere of the sun, or from the meteorites (especially the carbonaceous chondrites, which seem to be the most primitive) or from the stars of Population I or from the cosmic rays. The matter is 99 per cent hydrogen and helium, with hydrogen atoms about 10 times as abundant as helium; there is very little lithium, beryllium, or boron; lots of carbon, nitrogen, oxygen, fluorine, and especially neon; and from there on the abundance decrease irregularly, but in a defined, and at least partially understood pattern, in which the more stable atoms are the more numerous. Tables of cosmic abundances were first prepared in the 1930s, when the scheme was called the Russell mixture; the subject was invigorated by the Suess-Urey tables of the early 1950s and later development has been rapid and successful. Since these abundances are undoubtedly the result of nuclear transmutations, it is clear that the prediction of isotope ratio is a part of the problem of the prediction of element abundance ratios. To nuclear process, one isotope differs from another about as much as one element differs from another. Hence the rather close consistency of most isotope ratios makes us feel that there is very likely a real meaning to the cosmic ratios of relative abundances of the elements.

EARTH'S ROCK SYSTEMS

In the crust of the Earth there is also a fairly well-known scheme of the abundances of the elements. To the city-dweller, it may seem surprising that such a thing is possible; he thinks of the contrast between seawater, limestone, sandstone, coal and iron ore, each of which forms a part of the Earth, and each of which is an impure variety of a certain chemical compound: H_2O, $CaCO_3$, SiO_2, C, and Fe_2O_3, respectively. To the geologist, however, it is clear that the vast majority of the solid portion of the Earth's crust is composed of rocks of two great kindreds: the basaltic rocks, which cover the oceanic basins, and the granitic rocks which form the continents. Excluding the sea, which is not a part of the crust, the geologist believes that a grab sample of the material of the crust taken anywhere is unlikely to be of one of these almost pure substances, and is much more likely to be a fair approximation to one of these two great kindreds. The differences between those two great rock systems play an important part in geological thinking; but when they are compared with the composition of the mantle of the Earth, or of its core or of the meteorites, these differences pale into insignificance; it is possible to define, by an appropriate mixture of these two, something that can reasonably be called the crustal composition of the Earth.

When we compare the crustal composition with the cosmic composition, certain differences leap to the eye. Obviously, since the crust is solid, it cannot contain 99 per cent permanent gases. It is no surprise, therefore, that the crustal composition is deficient, by comparison with the cosmic composition, in hydrogen, helium, nitrogen, neon, argon, kryton and xenon. These elements are called the atmophile (air-loving) elements. There are some surprises about the actual amounts of the deficiency; of this more later. In broad outlines, the same is true of the meteorites as it must be since they are solid.

But there is an important set of differences between the meteorites and the crust of the Earth. To understand these differences, it is necessary to keep in mind that when we melt up a batch of elements of the cosmic composition, minus the volatiles, we find that we have two liquids, which, like oil and water, do not mix. One of these is mostly iron, with other elements, especially metals, dissolved in it. The other is a mixture of the oxides of metals, in which the oxide of silicon, SiO_2 is the most important. This kind of separation will only occur if there is not enough oxygen to oxidize all the metal. It is the basis of the process used in a blast furnace in which iron ore is mixed with various silicates and with enough coke to carry away a lot of the oxygen, as CO_2. The pig iron forms as one liquid, and the slag forms on top of it as the other. Nearly all the oxides of metals are in the slag, and are insoluble in the pig iron; nearly all the pure metals are in the pig iron and are insoluble in the slag.

Elements which prefer to exist as free metals and which seek to dissolve in the pig iron are called siderophile (iron-loving) elements. Those which prefer to exist as oxides are called lithophile elements. Obviously it is the elements with the least affinity for oxygen which will go into the pig iron; those with a high affinity for oxygen will go into the slag. Thus the siderophile elements are those which used to be called the noble elements (because they could not be corrupted by rust) while the lithophile elements are generally speaking the base metals.

WHERE THE GOLD IS

In the Earth's crust, the siderophile elements—gold, platinum and so forth—are markedly deficient. The usefulness of the gold standard rests on the fact that we do not expect ever to find a mountain made of gold. In meteorites, these elements have approximately their cosmic abundances. In the carbonaceous chondrites, where there is no metallic phase, the nickel, for instance, is in the rock mass of the meteorite. In chondritic meteorites, there is still a normal abundance of the siderophile elements, if we consider the meteorite as a whole. But in these meteorites there is not enough oxygen to oxidize all the metal, and as a result there is both a rocky, silicate phase and a metal phase, the two being coarsely intermingled. They have not really mixed; they are immiscible, like oil and water. And we find that the siderophile elements are hundreds or thousands of times as abundant in the metallic phase of the meteorites as in the silicate phase.

Why is the Earth's crust deficient in noble metals? Geochemists have believed for many years that the noble metals of the Earth followed the Earth's iron down to the core, when the core was formed. There is sound evidence for a dense core, apart wholly from the geochemical evidence; the overall density of the Earth, the Earth's moment of inertia, and its behavior toward seismic waves all suggest a dense core. Since iron is the only common element which is also dense, it is hard to resist the suggestion that the Earth, like the chondritic meteorites, has an iron and a silicate phase. It was suggested by N. F. Ramsey in 1948 that the Earth's core is a liquid phase of the silicates of the mantle; but this suggestion does not seem to meet the tests which have been devised for it. Francis Birch remarks that "if there is one hypothesis in geophysics which can be disproved, it is the hypothesis that the core of the Earth consists of the same material as the mantle."

BREAKUP VS. CAPTURE

We now see how we can distinguish between a moon formed by breakup of the Earth and one captured from the outside. If the moon was formed by fission, then the fission presumably occurred after the formation of the Earth's core, since the density of the moon, of 3.34 g/cm^3, is very close to the density of the Earth's mantle.

If we could compare the composition of the mantle of the Earth with the composition of the moon's interior, we would have a direct test of the fission hypothesis.

Unfortunately, we do not have samples of the Earth's mantle which are universally accepted as such; and we are not likely to get samples of the moon's interior in the first landing. In both cases, we must deal with differentiation products. Through terrestrial volcanism, some of the material of the Earth's interior comes to the surface. In the case of the Hawaiian Islands, it has been possible to follow, by seismic studies, the course of a glob of lava all the way from deep in the mantle up to its eruption in Mauna Loa. Yet the material erupted is not, we feel sure, a typical sample of the mantle. It represents, we believe, the liquid fraction of the mantle, wrung out from more solid material like salt water from a bathing suit.

Even though the argument must be indirect, however, it may be reliable. Though we do not have the ability to calculate what type of basalt will come from a given type of mantle rock, we do know that the constitution of the basalt depends on the constitution of the mantle rock. Hence if we should find that the differentiated rocks of the lunar crust resemble closely the rocks of the terrestrial crust, it would be a reliable indication that the lunar interior resembles the Earth's mantle. The critical point here is not the major elements: if a low-melting-point rock is to form at all, there must be certain resemblances in the major elements. It is the minor elements which give the show away. The first portion of a silicate mass to melt is sure to be enriched in alumina and impoverished in magnesia, for example, compared with meteoritic composition. But whether that mass will contain nickel or not, or gold or not, depends on how much there was in the primary material. So a close match to terrestrial composition would, as A. E. Ringwood has remarked, mean that the fission hypothesis is probably correct.

If, on the other hand, the trace elements proved to have an entirely different composition, perhaps with much more of the siderophile elements, then it would suggest that the moon was a captured body. H. C. Urey has, for example, drawn a parallel between the carbonaceous chondrites and the moon. In the silicate portions of these meteorites, the siderophile elements are reasonably abundant. We would expect that in a basalt derived from a carbonaceous chondrite, there would be much more gold, platinum, etc.

NOBLE ELEMENTS CLUE

One alternative can be promptly disposed of. It is very improbable that the moon has an iron core at all comparable with that of the Earth. The density of the moon corresponds closely to the density which is found in two other primitive silicate masses, namely the mantle of the Earth and the silicate portion of chondritic meteorites. The moment of inertia has recently been shown to correspond closely to that for a homogenous body (0.4 Mr^2 where M is the mass and r the radius; the earth has 0.33 Mr^2). There is no magnetic field, as we would expect for a molten core; and there is no evidence of metallic conductivity in the interior, as we would expect with a network of metal such as exists in a chondritic meteorite.

Hence it cannot be that the noble elements of the moon's material are stored in a core within the moon. If they are missing from the crust, in a pattern like that of the Earth, they were probably removed from the material of the moon's interior before the moon separated from the Earth. If the moon did not separate from the Earth, but is a captured body, then we will see in its crust a significantly different pattern of noble-element abundances.

There is a fourth group of elements to which we have not yet referred. These are the chalcophile (sulfur-loving) elements, so-called for historic reasons. The real significance of the chalcophile elements is now believed to be that they are volatile, like the atmophile elements, only less so. The deficiency of chalcophile elements may therefore reflect a period of stern outgassing of the

Earth, probably due to severe heating. The pattern of rare-gas deficiency points in the same direction; the lighter the gas, the greater the deficiency. This cannot be the consequence of something which happened when the whole Earth was gaseous, because in that case oxygen would have been driven off just like neon. In fact, oxygen is only slightly depleted, while neon is depleted by a huge factor. This seems to mean that the event took place after the oxygen became bound to the metals in the silicates of the mantle.

The moon ought to show traces of a similar event if the event was either the capture of the moon or its birth from the Earth. It should be found to be more deficient than the Earth in water, sulfides, carbon compounds, and so forth. Because of its small size, the gravitational disturbances accompanying either mode of origin ought to have caused greater distortions in the moon than in the Earth, and therefore there would be more heating and outgassing.

Thus it appears that the returned lunar sample may give us, for the first time, a real basis for theories about the origin of the moon. It also appears that it may cast light on the first billion years of the Earth's history. Perhaps the event of −3.5 billion years corresponds to capture of the moon by the Earth, with all the deep seated tidal disturbances which that would entail. Perhaps it corresponds to the fission of the Earth, with the ensuing heating (up to several thousand degrees) by tidal friction. The study of the trace element abundances, especially those of the siderophile elements, should tell the story.

UREY'S THEORY

Whichever view triumphs in this matter, it is probable that there will be a strong effect on our ideas about the origin of the solar system. For example, Harold C. Urey has long regarded the moon as a primitive object—one of a group of bodies a thousand miles or so in radius, out of which the planets and the meteorites formed. A demonstration that the moon is a captured body would bolster this idea. Along with this is the notion that some classes of meteorites come from the moon. Since meteorites play a critical role in our thinking about the origin of the solar system, it is clearly vital to know whether any of them come from the moon.

On the other hand, if the fission theory is found to be correct, it may conceivably lead to a new approach to the origin of the solar system. Most of the theories now in vogue for the origin of the solar system consider it to be the result of condensation of an original nebula surrounding the sun, to which the name of the solar nebula is given. The planets are imagined to be the result of a hierarchical system of aggregations, from atoms to molecules to smoke particles to large lumps. I would like to suggest that it is much easier to tear down a planet than to build one up. I admit that it is possible to think of ways by which atoms can be assembled into molecules in the solar system, and it is possible to think of ways by which large planets can grow by the accretion of meteorites. But there is no reasonable explanation of the way in which objects ranging from molecular to lunar size can grow in a normal solar-system environment. Recently V. V. Radzievsky and S. J. Paddack have shown that even radiation pressure may destroy bodies under a few centimeters in size. If the vector force due to radiation does not pass through the center of mass of the object, there will be a torque. Under reasonable assumptions about the albedo (Radzievsky) or the geometry (Paddack) the effect will be to cause spinup, leading to rational bursting in a few thousand years.

For objects in this range, the available evidence indicates that their life history is one of destruction. Meteorites bear datable marks of breakup; asteroids belong to families (the Hirayama groups) each of which is usually presumed to represent the breakup of a parent body; a dozen comets have been observed to divide. If to this evidence we add evidence that the moon at least is the product of the fission of a planet, then there will be a great temptation, at least to some people, to think of the solar system in terms of planetary fission rather than in terms of accretion from a solar nebula. They will remember G. P. Kuiper's idea that Pluto is an escaped satellite of Neptune. Conceivably Pluto was originally formed by the fission of Neptune; its high density might then result from the fact that Pluto somehow got a large share of the material of the iron core of the proto-planet. There will be a temptation to ascribe a considerable role to fission as a formative process in the solar system; Lyttleton suggested some years ago that Mars might have resulted from the fission of a planet; and Mercury is often thought of as naked core material. Conceivably the new data on the moon might give rise to a new and successful approach to the problem of the origin of the solar system.

TO MAKE PEBBLES SPEAK

A fundamental understanding of the functioning of the solar system is vital to the use of solar-system data to understand the origin of the universe. It is customary to think of problems of cosmology as the province of radio telescopes, and their smaller optical brothers. But the material of the pebble on the lawn also passed through the furnace in which the elements were made; if we knew enough, we could read the history of the universe in its structure. Historically, cosmology has been greatly influenced by geological thinking; in fact it was that fact that gave the initial impetus to geology in its earliest years. More recently, cosmology has been concerned with events prior to -4.7 billion years; and on these, geology and terrestrial geochemistry have little to say. But if we understood better the origin of the solar system, it might well be that we could make the pebble speak its piece.

THORNTON PAGE

12.   A VIEW FROM THE OUTSIDE

I like to think of myself as a "big-telescope man"—
ground-based, of course—but I have to admit that getting outside the atmosphere for a better look, and bringing home samples of astronomical bodies, beats anything
the Palomar telescope now can offer. In addition, space
exploration is influencing a shift in world public opinion
toward recognizing other abilities than military power as
an index of a nation's prestige. Concern about sizes of
standing armies, or numbers of battleships or squadrons
of bombers has waned, and missions to the moon now
somewhat outshine the (related) ability to fire ICBMs
and ABMs. Surely it is significant that world-wide interest in the Apollo lunar landing cut across political and
religious boundaries, so that more people were concerned
with it than have ever been concerned with one activity
in the whole history of mankind.

It also provided another frontier, replacing our old
western frontier that was overrun thirty to forty years
ago. President Kennedy recognized, and many econo-
mists agree, that the American public needs such a frontier to stimulate our inventiveness and productivity.
Aside from these rewards, NASA's space effort offers vast
new opportunities for astronomers and other scientists.
Observations and experiments with spacecraft can be
roughly classified in four categories:

1. Downward-looking Earth surveillance for meteorology (cloud patterns for weather prediction, high-alti-
tude conditions, auroras, etc.); for oceanography (ther-

mal and other data for mapping ocean currents); for geology (mapping, discovery of new landforms, locating mineral deposits); for agriculture (following seasonal plant growth, rainfall, drought, etc.) and for navigation and communications (aids to ships and aircraft).

2. Geophysical observations of the Earth's magnetosphere, the solar wind, solar flares and solar corona.

3. Solar system exploration, including: interplanetary medium (analysis of meteoroids and solar wind); accurate mapping of the moon, Mars, other planets and satellites; planetary atmospheres; and material sampling (lunar surface, Mars, comets, other planets and satellites).

4. Sidereal observations of more distant astronomical bodies, including: observation in the far ultraviolet, X-rays, and gamma-rays; high-resolution photography; deep infra-red observations; primary cosmic-ray measures; and radio observations, including very-long-base-line interferometry.

Enthusiasts can get carried away to science-fiction extremes on some of these topics, and specialists have written whole books on several of them. I'll try to stick to definite astronomical advances, admitting that unexpected discoveries may lead to a great deal more. The downward surveillance jobs may seem to be "services," rather than research observations. However, worldwide weather mapping has already contributed greatly to understanding the Earth's atmosphere, and the vast amounts of information soon to be collected about the Earth's surface will doubtless have a similar effect in geology. Mapping data from Earth orbiters have already revealed several old craters, probably of meteoric origin. The large numbers of TV images radioed down to a world-wide network of ground-based receivers require a good deal of computer time, and are complicated by cloud cover and other changes. In fact, the oceanographers, geologists and biologists are having to develop new techniques of data handling in order to get all the significant information from the pictures.

EARTH-WATCHING

Earth surveillance is generally done from unmanned satellites in low orbits—a few hundred miles above the surface, with periods from 90 to 110 minutes. Some geological data have been obtained on manned flights, also. This outside view of planet Earth offers some obvious advantages, but suffers a few observational difficulties. If a satellite passes through the auroral zones or the magnetic anomaly over Brazil and the South Atlantic, about 30° S. Latitude, it is subjected to fairly intense radiation from the Van Allen belt, which would fog any photographic emulsion aboard, and which requires shielding of photoelectric equipment. The early navigational satellites were (and are) also in low orbits, but soon there will be new ones in synchronous orbits (24-hour period, 26,400 miles from the center of the Earth). There is now such demand for synchronous satellites that in a few years there will be a traffic problem 22,000 miles above the equator, with communications and navigational satellites spaced a few hundred miles apart all the way around.

The low-level satellites have less of a traffic problem. The small atmospheric drag slowly brings each one down into the atmosphere, where it finally burns up. Still, there are over 1,000 objects now orbiting the Earth—many of them accurately tracked by the Smithsonian network of 16 ground-based Schmidt cameras which are located in the United States, Canada, Hawaii, Japan, Australia, India, Ethiopia, South Africa, Spain and South America, and controlled by the Smithsonian Astrophysical Observatory in Cambridge, Massachusetts. There are also three NASA radar nets used for tracking active spacecraft. One, called STADAN, has 15 stations in 10 different countries and four ships at sea, most of them with 85-foot dish antennas. The second is the NASA Manned Spacecraft Net of over 20 large S-band receivers, located in a dozen countries around the world. The third is the Deep Space Net of three receivers with 210-foot dishes in three different countries.

GEOPHYSICAL OBSERVATIONS

Although the Earth, in one sense, is an astronomical body, the conventional astronomy involved with satellites is primarily orbital. Motions of the low-level satellites, corrected for perturbations caused by the moon and sun and by other planets, have established the gravity field of the Earth with high precision, as well as the drag (or density) of the high atmosphere. The upper boundary of the Earth's atmosphere is vague; the ionosphere is best considered as part of the "magnetosphere" and the newly discovered low-frequency radio storms (of undetermined origin) probably belong there too.

The "near-Earth environment" has come to mean the Earth's magnetosphere and its interaction with the sun through radiation and particle streams—subjects which have developed rapidly in the past 10 years. Sounding rockets and long-orbit satellites have provided a wealth of data on the solar electro-magnetic spectrum, on the Earth's magnetic field, and on particles (ions and electrons) moving in it. They established the nature of the solar cosmic rays as high-energy protons shot out of the sun, together with a surprisingly high proportion of helium ions.

The "Van Allen belts" of lower-energy ions, moving under the influence of the Earth's magnetic field, have been found to be a single doughnut-shaped region deformed by the "solar-wind" stream of ions from the sun, so that there is a "shockfront" on the sunward side with a "magnetic sheath" about 15,000 miles thick. The Earth's magnetic field is confined to the "magnetosphere" that is elongated down-wind some 50,000 miles. This complex region, dominated by the solar wind and the Earth's magnetic field, has become a model for other planets that have magnetic fields. It is also a detector of violent activities in the solar atmosphere ("flares"), which produce erratic changes lower in our atmosphere, and affect radio transmission there by the effects of their gamma rays, X-rays, and far-ultraviolet radiation.

The time dependence of solar activity (11-year cycle) and rapid fluctuation with each flare (in a minute or less) characterize solar physics and geophysics. Most astronomical phenomena are less variable, although astrophysics has recently produced one-second pulsars, and quasars with weekly variations. The current NASA geophysical program, involving over 110 sounding rockets each year, Orbiting Solar Observatories (OSO) and other Earth orbiters, is collecting timed data on changes in the magnetosphere, the bow wave in front, and the "plasma tail" behind the Earth. It is planned to send "Solrad" missions toward the sun (to within 30 million miles) and Pioneer missions two million miles out in other directions to measure the solar wind during the quiet-sun years, 1971 to 1975. An important result of all this will be to map as accurately as possible the "geocorona" of hydrogen, which is escaping from the Earth much faster than expected. This local cloud causes a strong sky glow in the far-ultraviolet hydrogen emission line (Lyman-alpha, at 1261A), and hampers astrophysical observations of distant objects from the vicinity of the Earth.

THE SOLAR SYSTEM

Most of the exciting new astronomical advances are now being made in the exploration of the solar system, particularly by the lunar orbiters, the Apollo lunar missions, and the Mariner Mars missions. There are interconnections between these and other NASA programs which are very complex, and no one man in NASA has them all in mind. The central scientific goal is to obtain data related to the origin of the solar system, a topic that has intrigued men for the last three or four thousand years. Skipping early Babylonian and Greek theories that are rightly identified as the beginnings of physical science, there are two or three types of recent theories:

1. The Chamberlin-Moulton theory, proposed about 1900 with variants as late as 1940, in which the material

to form planets was pulled out of the sun by a low-probability chance event, such as the close passage of another star.

2. The Kant-Laplace theory, proposed in 1755 and modified by von Weizsäcker, Kuiper, Oort, and Urey in 1940–60, which predicts the formation of planets and comets whenever a gas cloud contracts to form a star like the sun.

3. The accretion theory, proposed about 1935 by Lyttleton, in which the sun picked up material for planets and comets as it passed by chance through inter-stellar clouds of gas and dust.

The first of these is by now pretty well eliminated; the second predicts that many other stars have planets where living organisms may have developed; and the third is more applicable to the formation of comets, which differ markedly from planets in their composition and their long, elliptical orbits around the sun. Most astronomers now favor the second, although the details of how different types of planets formed, four or five billion years ago, in eddies of gas and dust around the primitive sun are not fully worked out. An essential feature is the loss of low-density gas from the terrestrial planets (Mercury, Venus, Earth-moon, Mars and the asteroids). Hence the chemical composition of these bodies, and of the major planets (Jupiter, Saturn, Uranus and Neptune), is of great importance in confirming the theory. The temperature and composition of the primitive atmosphere around the Earth three or four billion years ago is the basis for the natural formation of amino acids, other organic material and the living organisms that evolved to present forms of life on Earth.

Studies of the interplanetary medium are based on the location and chemical composition of meteoroids, asteroids and other small chunks of solid material moving around the sun and having a bearing on the original dust from which the planets were formed. This material was contaminated by later material from comets, which are known to leave behind a kind of residue—small fragments (probably snow, wax and other fragile compounds) that we see as "meteor showers" when they hit the Earth's atmosphere. The solar wind, on the other hand, represents the composition of the solar atmosphere or corona. This wind "blows" outward the larger solid particles, while the smaller ones tend to spiral inward over long intervals because of the Poynting-Robertson effect of sunlight pressure.

Very small micro-meteoroids have been collected on many NASA satellites and found to be fewer in number than expected near the Earth. The long-distance Mariner space probes to Mars in 1969 and 1971, and to Jupiter about 1974, will determine whether there are more or fewer farther from the sun. Attempts will be made to photograph larger meteoroids on these Mariner missions, using cameras that have a range of a mile or so on small objects, up to millions of miles on large asteroids.

As expected, the solar wind is modified in the vicinity of the Earth by the outer atmosphere (ionosphere) and magnetic field. The moon has been found to have a "wake" related to its electrical properties. Special detectors will soon be flown on lunar flights to measure the helium, neon and argon composition of the solar wind, and to confirm the Earth's "bow wave" and the moon's "wake."

THE MOON

After the Russians received the first photos of the moon's backside in 1959, NASA launched several lunar orbiters with TV cameras that mapped the whole lunar surface at high resolution (to a few meters, as against the one-kilometer resolution of the best ground-based photos). These TV photos were radioed back to a new set of three sensitive receivers—in California, Australia and Spain—called the Deep Space Network, itself an engineering triumph.

By measurement of the Doppler shift in the lunar-orbiter radio signal received at Goldstone, California, mathematicians at the NASA-California Institute of

Technology Jet Propulsion Laboratory were able to compute orbits in 1968, and accurately map the gravity field of the moon. To their surprise, the maps showed seven broad gravity anomalies above the large circular maria, possibly indicating that there are huge blocks of high-density material or mass concentrations about 50 kilometers below the maria. These "mascons" are a puzzle in themselves, since the moon's internal strength must be unexpectedly large to hold them in place for any length of time. If they are remains of large, dense bodies that hit the moon and formed the maria, they must be hundreds of millions—or billions—of years old, yet they have not sunk to the center. Alternatively, the measured gravity anomalies may be caused by lunar surface topography only (that is, the dense "mascons" don't exist).

The small lunar craters measured on the orbiter photos confirmed their meteoritic origin, and other features resembling winding stream beds are apparent on these photos. Harold Urey, D. H. Menzel and a few others consider it likely that there was once free-flowing liquid water on the moon (*Bulletin of the Atomic Scientists*, April 1969), and Menzel has shown that the moon probably retained an atmosphere for many millions of years. That atmosphere is now generally considered to be less than 10^{-13} of the Earth's atmospheric density, although recent studies of lunar orbiters give some evidence of density as high as 10^{-8} of the Earth's. The presence of water or ice on the moon is not generally accepted by geologists. Studies of the craters gave a fair idea of the distribution of meteor sizes in the past, and distinguished newer craters overlapping older ones, including the maria.

LUNAR SURFACE MATERIAL

One controversy that arose in the early sixties concerned the nature of the lunar surface material—whether it is meteoric dust, as proposed by T. Gold, or lava, as proposed by G. P. Kuiper, or volcanic ash, as proposed by E. Shoemaker and others. Its optical and thermal properties (reflectivity and low heat conductivity) have been fairly well determined from ground-based observations. The dust hypothesis rests on the meteoric bombardment—hundreds of millions of small meteoroids per day, presumed to be about the same as those we see as meteors in the Earth's atmosphere, but striking the lunar surface at speeds of about 10 miles per second. None of these can be large, since no new crater has appeared on the front side of the moon in 200 years of telescope observations, but the many small impacts possibly chip away exposed lunar rocks, producing many tons of rock dust each year.

The lava and ash hypotheses are based on the observed lunar domes—low, rounded structures identified as extinct volcanoes—and several features that look like flows of lava or loose ashes. One spectrum of a bright patch in the crater Alphonsus, taken in the USSR by N. A. Kosyrev in 1958, showed hot gases there—the only evidence of current volcanic activity on the moon. In fact, ground-based low-frequency radio observations seem to indicate that the mantle of the moon to several miles' depth is freezing cold—an indication of ice under the lunar surface, rather than hot lava, and a rigid interior capable of supporting the mascons.

The dust-lava question was left unresolved in 1967 and 1968 when three Surveyor lunar landers obtained close-up TV photos of the terrain, and measured the composition, porosity, and bearing-strength of the "soil" under the landers. There were several chunky rocks nearby, and the "soil" characteristics were consistent with basaltic rock dust about the size of sand grains. However, no new dust is evident, and the selenologists felt that a definite conclusion must await the analysis of the samples returned to Earth by the Apollo lander this year.

Starting in 1967 at the NASA Manned Spacecraft Center near Houston, Texas, an elaborate Lunar Receiving Lab (LRL) was constructed. At the suggestion of the National Academy of Sciences, it was arranged to isolate the Apollo astronauts and their 5- to 90-pound sample of lunar "soil" as a guard against any living organism or other materials picked up on the moon which might harmfully contaminate the Earth's atmosphere before a complete analysis is made for organic material and the precise physical and chemical characteristics of the lunar "soil." In March 1969 the LRL was given a 30-day isolation test which showed that after some trouble with the vacuum working gloves everything worked satisfactorily.

Other preparations included the Lunar Science Institute (LSI) organized by the National Academy of Sciences, with W. W. Rubey of the University of California at Los Angeles as director. The LSI is inviting guest investigators from universities and other research centers around the world to propose studies involving the lunar samples or any other NASA data. The Institute plans to house up to 20 such guests in a building with offices and library about two miles from the Lunar Receiving Lab. Plans also include weekly meetings with scientists at the Manned Spacecraft Center in Houston, Rice University and the University of Houston, and guest lecturers.

MOONQUAKES AND LASERS

In addition to bringing back the first lunar samples, Apollo placed a seismometer on the moon to record "moonquakes," and a corner-reflector to return laser light signals. From the latter, the Earth-moon distance can be measured with an accuracy of 20 centimeters or less. Over a period of several months, the lunar orbit will be determined, and later deviations will show small effects such as gravity waves absorbed by the Earth-moon system. In nine later landings, seismic sounding devices and sensitive magnetometers will be emplaced at several locations, in maria and in mountains, and attempts will be made to measure for a period of one or two years the very small atmospheric pressure, cosmic rays, and heat flow from the moon's interior. Other instruments will probably be carried in the orbiting Command Service Modules, without landing them. These will measure lunar surface radiation over a wide band of wave lengths from gamma rays to infra-red, from circular orbit about 30 miles above the

lunar equator. The gamma rays will detect the low radioactive content of granite, and the infra-red detectors can
map the lunar surface temperatures accurately. It is
planned that astronauts will travel up to hundreds of
miles from their landing sites in specially designed vehicles and rocket-powered "jumpers" to study such lunar
surface geology ("selenology") as mountains, faults,
craters, and domes. Such exploratory trips will take up
to three full days, and may lead to the discovery of a site
suitable for a lunar underground shelter, where men can
live for several months, possibly operating an astronomical observatory.

All this will lead to a fairly comprehensive picture of
the moon: its internal structure, its surface material in
highlands and plains, the effect of meteoritic bombardment and its four-billion-year history.

MARS

Although Mars at closest approach is some 200 times
farther from the Earth than the moon, similar exploratory missions are already under way. In February and
March, Mariner 6 and 7 were launched to pass within
2,000 miles of Mars about August 1, radioing back TV
pictures of the surface with a resolution better than 100
feet. (In 1965, Mariner-4 got the first close-up pictures
at two-mile resolution, showing a barren landscape with
craters like the moon's.) In 1971, it is planned to map
the whole surface of Mars from two orbiters, and these
will be tracked accurately to get possible evidence of
gravity anomalies like the moon's mascons. Studies will
also be made of the surface in the infra-red, of the nature
of the dark features (now thought to be highlands and
mountains), of the blue atmospheric haze, and of the
two small moons, Deimos and Phobos. For 1973, two
unmanned Mars Viking landers are planned, with elaborate precautions against biological contamination, to
analyze the atmosphere and surface material, and to emplace a seismometer, which will send back records of
"Marsquakes" for a year or so. The overall picture of
Mars should then be almost as complete as the 1969

picture of the moon, and comparison of these two should show how conditions differed at two distances from the center of the primordial solar nebula during the last four billion years.

MAJOR PLANETS

The NASA Pioneer program should reach Jupiter in 1974. The distance is so great (500 million miles) that radio communications to Earth limit the amount of data that can be collected, and a large part of the mission will be spent en route. During this two-year interval, meteoroids and asteroids can be photographed, and cosmic-ray changes detected as Pioneer recedes from the Earth and sun. Close-up observations of Jupiter's atmosphere may clarify the source of its odd radio emission, and the nature of its belts and red spot.

From 1976 to 1978, Jupiter and the other major planets (Saturn, Uranus and Neptune) just happen to be lined up so that a single "Grand Tour" flight can be made by one spacecraft passing close to all four. Close-up photos, radio, radar, and magnetic measures can then be made to compare these giant planets, and to learn more about material at large distances from the sun.

All these, and later missions, will provide astronomers with detailed data on almost all of the solar system. Mention should also be made of the Mariner-5 close approach to Venus in 1965 which, together with the Russian missions down into Venus' atmosphere, established the high temperature and density there. It is also possible to fly a single mission close by Venus and on to Mercury, a planet whose peculiar density and rotation are difficult to explain in any theory of the origin of the solar system.

Several unmanned Orbiting Solar Observatories (OSO) are now measuring the solar spectrum in the far ultraviolet, and detecting the changes caused by solar flares and sunspots. Other possible future missions include a shot through the head of a comet, which will establish its structure and mass (today a matter of guesswork), and orbital observations to test gravitational mechanics. For instance, accurate tracking of the Mariner probes in their later orbits around the sun in 1972 will determine radio frequency changes and deflections when Mariner is viewed past the sun, and provide a check on general relativity.

BEYOND THE SOLAR SYSTEM

Of course, the stars are too distant for return trips to be made by spacecraft during my lifetime, but the advantages of observing them from above the Earth's atmosphere are considerable. The whole development of astronomy, up to 1940, was based on observations in a small part of the electromagnetic spectrum (visual and photographic light, mostly of wave lengths 3,000 to 10,000 angstroms) through the turbulent air above our ground-based observatories. In 1940, radio observations were added, and in 1952 ultraviolet observations from rockets. Now, from NASA's Orbiting Astronomical Observatory, observations may in principle be made at any wave length, and vast amounts of new data are suddenly available to the astronomer.

The first job, delayed several years by a mechanical breakdown in the first Orbiting Astronomical Observatory (OAO), is to measure the ultraviolet spectra of many different types of stars from 3,000 to 1,000 angstroms or so (a limit set by optical difficulties). Two groups of astronomers, one at the University of Wisconsin and one at the Smithsonian Astrophysical Observatory in Cambridge, Massachusetts, are doing this right now with eight telescopes of 8- to 16-inches aperture in the second OAO. (Early this year, the 16-inch telescope and one 8-inch failed.) As expected, the hot, blue stars are very bright in the far ultraviolet. Unfortunately, local clouds of hydrogen emit strong Lyman-alpha radiation that has swamped all efforts to observe faint objects at that important wave length. These local hydrogen clouds, possibly a single, smooth "geocorona" extending thousands of miles above Earth's atmosphere, are now being studied by OAO observers. The local clouds set new requirements for astronomical observatories far from the Earth.

After the preliminary survey is completed this year,

we will know from OAO observations the characteristic spectra from 1,000 to 10,000 angstroms of the "ordinary" main-sequence stars classed as O, B, A, F, and G types, as well as of several giants and supergiants. Spectral measures of a few nebulae (luminous gas clouds) will also be extended to 1,000 angstroms, and I have asked for galaxy spectra (several already obtained), from which I hope to derive the composition of galaxies—how many stars of various types they contain, and how much gas.

Later OAOs will add gamma-ray, X-ray, and infra-red measures, some of which have already been made from high balloon flights and short-duration sounding rockets. These will significantly extend spectroscopic data down to 0.01 A, and up to 500,000 A (50 mu). Each piece of observing equipment requires more than three years for design and manufacture. The measures must be digitized (coded for radio transmission to Earth), far-infra-red detectors must be cooled to liquid helium temperatures, and all parts must be tested under spacecraft conditions to avoid the "zero results" of a failure. Preliminary designs have been drafted for larger reflecting telescopes, up to 120-inch aperture. Not only will these be able to analyze light in the full spectral range, they can get pictures of much higher resolution than is possible from the ground through the Earth's turbulent atmosphere. Such high precision in measuring the direction to stars will give better measures of their distances and motions, as well as the sizes and shapes of nebulae. All this is true of planets, their moons, comets, and asteroids, too.

MANNED OBSERVATIONS

Although unmanned orbiters and space probes have produced so much—and can be used to produce far more astronomical observation—NASA has wisely planned for manned observatories outside the Earth's atmosphere, where "resident observers" can repair equipment breakdowns, modify instruments after new data are obtained, and react quickly to new developments. There are even plans to try manufacturing processes under zero-gravity conditions. Of course, the presence of men has certain disadvantages for astronomical observations; their body movements disturb a spacecraft, and their biological requirements (air, food and water) complicate the space-craft design. The first of these disadvantages can be avoided by separating (or uncoupling) the telescope mount from the spacecraft, or by placing the telescope on the moon, but the contamination of a space environ-ment by leaks of air and other gases, including sewage disposal, has yet to be eliminated by design improve-ments.

Nevertheless, plans are being considered for an Earth Orbiting Scientific Lab (EOSL) with a 36-inch tele-scope, spectrograph and other equipment, and a crew of two or three men, or an even larger space station with dozens of men aboard which would rendezvous with supply ships. After the lunar surface is explored further next year, a suitable site for a manned observatory may be discovered, where living quarters can be provided underground, shielded from extreme temperature changes, meteoric bombardment, and cosmic rays. Of course, the re-supply would be more difficult at 240,000 miles than at several hundred miles for the EOSL, but materials on the moon—especially ice, if it is found there —may save re-supply weight.

Sidereal observations from EOSL or a lunar observa-tory (or from OAO and other unmanned spacecraft) will certainly add to our understanding of the universe. They will augment and extend the direct exploration of Mars, Venus, Jupiter, comets and asteroids, as well as the other planets, the stars, nebulae, and galaxies. Radio observations will also be involved, even though ground-based radio telescopes are doing fairly well as is. (They miss the submillimeter and very long waves absorbed by the Earth's ionosphere, and suffer increasing interference from TV stations and other earthly radio noise.) Radio telescopes in orbit can get the rest of the electro-mag-netic spectrum, and one on the far side of the moon could avoid earthly noise. Of considerable interest right now would be the very high resolution possible by com-bining the signals received from widely separated radio telescopes—possibly one on the moon and one on Earth. Such a long-base interferometer could resolve fine structure in the smallest radio sources, to solve the riddle of the fluctuating quasars, thought to be the most distant objects we can now observe.

PART IV

THE TECHNOLOGICAL IMPACT

FRANKLIN A. LONG

13. THE INDUSTRIAL IMPACT OF APOLLO

The aerospace industry of the United States produces virtually all of the rockets, spacecraft and associated equipment employed in the National Aeronautics and Space Administration's Apollo program for a manned lunar landing. The same industry also manufactures commercial aircraft as well as sophisticated military aircraft and other technical equipment used by the Department of Defense. The Apollo program has completed the first manned landing on the moon and is now entering the follow-on phase of a slower-paced continuing program of lunar exploration. Hence, it is very much in order to ask what impact these climactic events will have on the aerospace industry. But before doing this it may be useful to examine more carefully just what constitutes the aerospace industry.

It is easy enough to identify a number of companies which obviously fall into the aerospace category. These are the large companies which are heavily involved with aircraft manufacturing and which do a large fraction of their business for agencies of the federal government. Companies like Boeing and McDonnell-Douglas come immediately to mind. Table 13–1 lists several of these obvious candidates and also includes figures on their annual sales and their rank in Fortune magazine's 1968 list of the 500 largest corporations of the United States. Clearly all of these are large and potent corporations. All of them have played very substantial parts in the civilian space program of NASA.

There are a number of other large U.S. corporations

Table 13–1

Company	Annual Sales $\$ \times 10^{-9}$	Corporate Rank
McDonnell-Douglas	2.93	16
Boeing	2.88	19
North American Rockwell .	2.44	28
Lockheed Aircraft	2.34	30
General Dynamics	2.25	32

which are very substantially involved in Department of Defense business and in NASA business but which, at the same time, are deeply involved in the civilian economy. Typical examples are the General Electric Company and IBM. Both of these corporations are vital to the nation's defense and space efforts and yet their large role in civilian enterprises makes it inappropriate simply to label them as aerospace companies.

Another aspect of the aerospace business is the large number of small businesses whose activities link closely to defense and space. NASA officials have stated that the NASA space programs involve the efforts of about 50,000 companies. The vast majority of these are relatively small and act as subcontractors to larger corporations in the supply of such specialty items as electronics gear, components for guidance systems, transistors which may be used in computers, etc. Since these companies also supply equipment to corporations doing predominantly civilian business, e.g., to General Motors, it is almost impossible to classify them strictly as aerospace industry. Since this is also true to a lesser degree for the larger corporations, the category is inescapably a fuzzy one. Even so, the concept of the aerospace industry as a technologically sophisticated group of corporations, strongly oriented toward design and production in government military and space efforts, is a useful one.

All of the large aerospace companies have a variety of capabilities. Very commonly they compete with each other for major defense and space contracts. Even so, certain of them have become well-known for specific products. Thus, Boeing is particularly well-known for its B-52 bombers, for commercial jet transport aircraft and for its central role in the development of the Minuteman missile system. General Dynamics produced the Atlas rockets which formed the basis for the first generation intercontinental ballistic missile (ICBM) systems; more recently it has been producing the F-111 Bombers. Lockheed Aircraft is currently in the news as the producer of the immense C-5 military transport aircraft.

Similarly, individual large aerospace companies have become identified as the manufacturers of particular major components of the Apollo system. Grumman Aircraft has been responsible for the Lunar Module, the spacecraft which actually carried the astronauts down to the surface of the moon. North American Rockwell has produced the Command and Service Modules for the Apollo spacecraft. Its Rocketdyne division produces important rocket engines including the largest of them all, the F-1 engine which, using liquid oxygen and kerosene as fuels, produces 1.5 million pounds of thrust. The McDonnell side of McDonnell-Douglas produced the Gemini spacecraft. The Douglas portion has produced the S-IVB third stage for the Saturn V rocket launch system.

Here, then, is a large industry with great capabilities for building sophisticated airplanes, radars and related equipment, and which is the principal supplier of equipment for NASA. This interrelationship raises a number of important questions. A first general question is, what benefits has the civilian space business brought to the aerospace industry and through it to the nation? As a specific part of this question one can ask what technological "spin-off" (or in Ralph Lapp's interesting phrase, "drip-off") there may have been from the space activities to the defense-oriented and civilian activities of these companies. A second general question is, what will it mean to these companies if the current slowdown of activity within NASA continues? More specifically, what will be the consequences if the Apollo manned flight program is terminated after the first eight or ten flights to the moon, i.e., after the currently programmed group of Saturn V rockets and associated spacecraft is exhausted?

MISSILES AND SPACE ROCKETS

A preliminary point to make is that the aerospace industry would be deeply involved in the space business even if there were no such thing as NASA. This is so for two rather different reasons. First, much of the equipment that goes into ICBM systems is very similar to the equipment used for space programs. The launch rockets used with ICBMs have the capability to put substantial payloads into Earth orbit and indeed to launch small payloads which escape Earth's gravity and probe the moon and outer planets. Similarly, the guidance systems used for intercontinental missiles and the tracking systems used to follow their behavior are close cousins to the analogous systems that are used for space efforts.

Even more relevant, however, is the existence of a very substantial U.S. military space program, a program which in recent years has been roughly one-fourth as large as the NASA effort. The magnitude of the defense-oriented space activity may well be on the increase and since there is a strong probability that the NASA effort will decrease in size, the relative importance of the defense space effort will almost surely grow. The design and manufacture of components for the military space program are almost totally in the hands of the companies of the aerospace industry. Hence, it is virtually certain that this industry will be in the space business for the indefinite future.

Let us then consider the impact of the space business as a whole on the aerospace industry. An important point is that the essential "style" of production of components for space use is significantly different from that for the production of aircraft. The "production run" of the major items to be used for space use is usually very small —in numbers of twos or tens rather than hundreds. Reliability requirements are exceedingly high and production specifications are, of course, correspondingly tight. Once the design and manufacture of a particular set of space vehicles are completed, the next job to be done may be of a very different character indeed. All of this means that manufacture of space components calls for exceedingly large efforts in design and supervision by trained engineers and a smaller but necessarily meticulous manufacturing effort. These facts lead to very high costs per pound. Much of this contrasts with aircraft where a particular model may be produced in the hundreds and where an improved but basically similar model may follow on after a first one.

The sophisticated character of space equipment implies that its manufacture will contribute importantly to the technical capabilities of the aerospace industries. The engineers involved will be competent in the design of components for exacting performance and with very high reliability. Similarly, production groups will be trained in the manufacture of products to highly exacting standards. It is reasonable to assume that the skills which are developed will be of substantial importance to the manufacture of other technically demanding products for uses other than in space.

SPIN-OFF FROM SPACE

The development of enhanced industrial skills is only one aspect of the often discussed "technological spin-off." The more commonly quoted aspects are the new products, new materials and new manufacturing procedures that presumably arise from the space effort and that are then consequential to the nation's other civilian efforts. The space program has assuredly made contributions of this sort. In its reports to Congress, NASA has often pointed to specific items which the nation has acquired from its space programs, many of them developed within the aerospace industry. A few of these are obvious. Thus, miniaturization of electronic components is vital to the space effort as a way to save weight and as a way to increase reliability. This same miniaturization is directly applicable to civilian programs. Another major consequence of the space effort has been the development of a variety of special purpose digital computers with sophisticated accompanying computer "software" programs. These developments will undoubtedly find uses in the non-space civilian efforts. One can argue that these "spin-off" benefits are of prime importance to the aerospace industry and through it to the nation and that a diminution of their development will be harmful. However, this is a dubious argument. Since the very magnitude of the spin-off effect is almost impossible to determine, it seems idle to try to decide whether spin-off is greater from a space program than from a military program or indeed from a civilian production program. Technological spin-off is a benefit but is not one which can easily be quantified, catalogued or predicted.

There are indirect benefits to the aerospace industries from their participation in the dramatic and frequently glamorous space program. The press releases and advertisements from these industries put large stress on their efforts in the NASA space programs. Presumably, this is because the "image" of an important contributor to an exciting and technologically demanding civilian program is one which the industries like and seek.

SPACE VEHICLES VS. AIRCRAFT

From a financial standpoint the impact of participation by the aerospace industry in space efforts has been substantial but very far from dominating. According to the magazine, Aviation Week, sales of the aerospace industry in 1968 were on the order of $27 billion. This represented a gradual build-up from a 1960 figure of roughly $20 billion. A rough estimate of aerospace sales to the space programs in 1968 is $4.5 billion to NASA and $1.2 billion to the military space program. Hence, the total space manufacturing effort represented no more than 25 per cent of the total effort of the aerospace industry and sales to NASA amounted to only about 15 per cent. Since the aircraft needs of the civilian air industry are expanding and since there is no sign of a let-up in the military expenditures in fields other than space, there is no reason to expect the percentage sales to the space programs to increase in the future. The importance of the civilian program of NASA may well decline and may in future years represent no more than 10 per cent of the total effort of this industry.

Dr. Bruno Augenstein, one of the experts of the Rand Corporation, has recently outlined the sales situation that will very probably hold in the decade of the 1970s. The total effort of the space program during these years will be in the order of $6 billion annually. Sales of new civilian aircraft and parts will perhaps average around $7 billion per year during this period. The level of spending for military production within the aerospace industry is less easy to evaluate but a reasonable estimate is somewhere between $12 and $16 billion per year. Finally, one can expect sales of non-aerospace products by the aerospace industry to be perhaps as large as $4 billion annually. In light of these various estimates, it is clear that substantial variations in sales for NASA for civilian space efforts will not perturb the aerospace industry greatly one way or another.

Nor does it appear likely that variations in the size of the civilian space effort will be particularly hard on any employee group within the industry. The current Apollo program has developed large numbers of engineers with special capabilities for space programs and large numbers of skilled workers for the manufacture of space equipment. However, all of the events of recent years have strongly indicated that these special skills are to a considerable degree transferable and that skilled workers in these fields are highly mobile. Thus, the phase-out of the Atlas rocket production at General Dynamics, the termination of production of civilian aircraft by the Convair plant at San Diego, the stoppage in production of B-52 bombers have all occurred without catastrophic impact on either the industrial concerns involved or the engineers and skilled workers. This is not to say that production cutbacks will not cause turmoil and difficulty for individual companies and for individual employees;

it only says that overall the effects of substantial fluctuations in the space business of the aerospace industry will not be catastrophic.

FUTURE LUNAR FLIGHTS

What then is the particular situation with the Apollo manned lunar mission and what does the future look like? The aerospace industry is still in the process of completing manufacture of the first "buy" of Apollo systems. This was for 15 Saturn V rocket launch systems, 12 Saturn IBs, and enough spacecraft to permit adequate systems testing and to provide an ample reserve for the actual lunar landing attempts. Current purchases give us enough Saturn V launch rockets and adequate numbers of Apollo Command and Service modules and Lunar Modules to permit eight to nine manned lunar landings to follow Apollo 11. At a launch rate of two missions per year this would extend the manned lunar exploration of the moon into 1974 or 1975. There are also enough Saturn IB launch systems available from the initial purchase so that in combination with components of the Apollo spacecraft system there can be several Earth-orbiting Apollo Applications flights in the early years of the 1970s. Actually, even with the currently rather limited Apollo Applications Program it is unclear whether some of the more ambitious components of it, most particularly an initial space station experiment, will be approved and funded by Congress. But even if the program is fully funded, it is planned to be carried out with use of the currently available spacecraft and launch systems.

UNMANNED PROBES LIKELY

As of this point in time, it seems inescapable that the rate of expenditure for equipment for the Apollo mission will drop drastically in the next year or two. Furthermore, there appears to be no obvious prospect that the expenditure level for NASA programs will build up again soon. It is conceivable that new discoveries will be made in the further manned lunar landings which will make a strong case for an extension of these manned landing efforts. This could lead to a further buy of Apollo hardware. It is also conceivable that something similar could happen with the Apollo Applications Program. The difficulty in this case is, however, that neither the rocket launch system for the Saturn V nor the Apollo spacecraft is particularly well-suited for Earth-orbital applications programs. It would seem to be at least as likely that in the mid- or late seventies further exploration of the moon will be done principally with unmanned space probes launched by significantly smaller launch systems and that Earth orbital programs will be almost exclusively carried out by the low-cost unmanned systems.

There will, of course, continue to be a space program in the 1970s and the aerospace industry will continue to have a major role. At a minimum there will be a variety of unmanned programs for the military and for the civilian space programs. Examples are: communication satellites, surveillance systems, weather watch, planetary probes and space astronomy. As an outgrowth of the Apollo Applications Program, a more or less continuously manned orbiting space station is a possibility. The interest in many of these programs will strongly depend on their cost-effectiveness. Hence, there will be major efforts to produce longer-lived satellites and more efficient launch systems. Major studies are now underway for low-cost booster systems whereby the cost of putting payloads into Earth orbit might be reduced by one or even two orders of magnitude. Within this set of possibilities will be found the components of the previously predicted $5 or $6 billion per year for the U.S. space program.

CATCHING THE BRASS RING

Actually, not all of this effort will be of direct benefit to the aerospace industry. A principal characteristic of NASA is the existence of substantial "in-house" technical capability, most of it concentrated in a half-dozen major research and development centers. Even in the driving Apollo program these centers have had important roles. Thus, the basic design and indeed prototype construction of much of the Saturn IB and Saturn V launch systems were done at the Marshall Space Flight Center. Similarly, the Jet Propulsion Laboratory at Pasadena, California, not a NASA center in the strictest sense, has played a major role in the design and production of unmanned space probes. The post-Apollo program of NASA may well consist principally of unmanned exploration of the moon and the planets, along with unmanned Earth-orbiting satellites for space sciences and space applications. If so, and under the pressure of tight budgets, there is a good possibility that much of the design and production of the spacecraft will occur in the NASA centers. The aerospace industry will continue to be the preferred instrument for programs of continued production—satellites for space communication and rockets for launch systems, and will continue to perform the large fraction of space business for the military, where the "in-house" capability is considerably smaller. But, for NASA, the fraction of design and production done in the centers may increase substantially.

The tantalizing "brass ring" for the aerospace industry and, for that matter, for NASA also, is the prospect of manned exploration of the planets, starting with Mars. Here is a program whose cost might be on the order of $100 billion for the Mars effort alone, and whose duration would be at least a decade. If fully accepted by the nation as a high priority goal, a Mars expedition could catalyze the entire space effort much as Apollo has done in the 1960s. The sheer magnitude of the effort would require extensive participation by the entire aerospace industry. Sales of space equipment could easily increase to $10 or $12 billion per year. Unfortunately for the supporters of a manned Martian mission, prospects for any early decision to go ahead appear very dim and even the long-term prospects do not appear bright. The current national mood is to focus on domestic problems. This may change in a few years, possibly as a positive response to successful manned lunar exploration, but it does not appear likely. Furthermore, greatly increased capability for exploration of the planets by unmanned space probes will almost surely be developed. As a result, and in the absence of some imaginative way to lower the costs of manned space efforts in a major way, the national interest in another large and expensive manned space effort may remain low.

Where will all this leave the aerospace industry? In pretty good shape, actually. Sale to space programs at a continuing level of $6 billion per year is not a bad prospect. And as commercial applications of orbiting satellites mature and grow, it is at least conceivable that a firm coupling to the nation's business will provide a more satisfactory base for space manufacture than either military programs or planetary exploration.

WERNHER VON BRAUN

14. SATURN/APOLLO AS A TRANSPORTATION SYSTEM

The first moon landing will undoubtedly give a strong lift to the spirit of mankind, for it was a bold, imaginative step in the endless exploration of the world about us. And it will undeniably boost the prestige of the United States, for it reflects the nation's technical and organizational strength.

The aura of adventure and the competitive gains to national prestige surrounding Project Apollo should not be ignored, for they helped to arouse and sustain widespread support for a mammoth and expensive undertaking, difficult to explain or justify in simple, earthly terms, which most likely would never have gotten off the ground on its scientific and technological merits alone.

The immediate scientific returns from the first manned lunar landing are necessarily limited. The real meaning of the first landing lies in its demonstration of this nation's manned space flight capability, started with one-man sub-orbital hops and brief orbital flights in Project Mercury, nurtured in two-man orbital missions up to two weeks in duration in Project Gemini, and expanded in Project Apollo to the point where three men could leave Earth, travel more than a quarter of a million miles through space, land on another celestial body, and return safely home. The lunar landing opened the door to direct observations by man throughout the solar system.

The deep space transportation system developed in Project Apollo includes the Saturn V launch vehicle, the three-module Apollo spacecraft and related ground support equipment for manufacturing, testing, launching and communications.

EVOLUTIONARY ADVANCES

The movement that resulted in the Saturn project was formally initiated on August 15, 1958, by the Advanced Research Projects Agency of the Department of Defense, when it authorized a research and development program at Redstone Arsenal, Huntsville, for a 1.5 million pound thrust booster, using a cluster of existing rocket engines.

The Saturn project was transferred to NASA (National Aeronautics and Space Administration) after its formation on October 1, 1958. And on January 25, 1962, NASA approved developments of the three-stage Saturn V for manned circumlunar flights and manned landings using the lunar orbital rendezvous method.

It was originally estimated that the Apollo spacecraft would weigh 45 or more tons. Starting with this mission requirement, we designed and built the Saturn V to place 140 tons into low Earth orbit or send 50 tons to the vicinity of the moon. For 10 years we have been concentrating much of our effort on developing this ability to place men and x number of pounds of payload into space. Now that this capability has been demonstrated satisfactorily, we can give more attention to its beneficial use.

No one knows what the final destiny of man in space will be, or if there will indeed be any limit to his explorations. Regardless of where the trail blazed by Apollo leads us, I am convinced that man's first footprint on the moon marks the beginning of a bright new era in space exploration. And I am just as certain that the advances of the future, like those of the past, will be entirely evolutionary, as we continually apply hard-won knowledge and experience to the solution of fresh and intriguing mysteries.

LIMITED FIRST MISSION

During the first lunar landing mission the astronauts remained on the moon's surface for less than one day. The time spent outside their lunar module was limited to approximately two hours, and they ventured only a short distance from their spacecraft. Since the primary purpose of this mission was to demonstrate an operational capability, a conservative approach was adopted.

The primary scientific objective of the first landing was to collect up to 80 pounds of lunar samples, for analysis by scientific investigators from 20 institutions in eight countries. The two men also emplaced simple equipment for three scientific experiments—a solar-powered seismometer for detecting moonquakes, an aluminum-foil detector for solar wind particles and a multi-piece glass mirror to reflect the light of ruby lasers mounted in telescopes on Earth. Astronomers of all nations should be able to direct their telescopes at the laser retro-reflector, enabling them to measure Earth-moon distances to an accuracy of six inches in 250,000 miles. Its use should increase our knowledge of the moon's size and shape, movements of the Earth's poles and possible drift of our continents. The moon itself is a very poor reflector, with an albedo of about 11 per cent.

In addition, live television pictures of lunar features and astronaut activities were transmitted to Earth.

FUTURE MISSIONS

NASA has plans ready for implementing a logical phasing of lunar exploration missions to follow this first landing.

The first phase of continued exploration would use immediately available Saturn V launch vehicles, Apollo spacecraft, and facilities funded by Apollo for investigating the two types of lowlands or maria and the two major classes of highlands.

The second phase would involve flights to more difficult sites, requiring pinpoint landing accuracy, increased mobility, longer staytime and greater payloads.

The third phase would consist of lunar orbital missions, using remote sensing instruments aboard the command and service modules to study the lunar surface.

And then one can envision the buildup of exploration capability by revisiting the same site on the moon. This in turn might lead to semipermanent and eventually permanent operation of a lunar base, complete with observatory and research facilities.

The eastern maria of the moon, which have a barely reddish tinge, are distinctly different from the western maria, which are slightly bluish in appearance. During the first follow-on missions the astronauts would emplace a more complex set of devices, called Apollo Lunar Surface Experiment Packages, each with a nuclear isotope power supply that would permit operation for one to two years. NASA's budget requests for fiscal year 1970 include the continuation of Apollo lunar missions at the rate of two or three flights a year.

Lunar Orbiter, Surveyor and Apollo photographs have identified many additional interesting landing sites, such as volcanic types, riverlike channelways, fracture zones and impact craters.

INCREASING CAPABILITY

The capability of the basic Apollo system must be increased to permit exploration of these additional sites. The first requirements are improved astronaut mobility, longer staytimes on the surface and expanded instrumentation.

Astronaut mobility can be advanced by the use of a constant-volume suit which would reduce the amount of energy expended by the astronaut in moving about. Improvements in joint design would incorporate rotary bearings, rolling convolutes and constant-volume bellows. A new suit would not be an entirely new development effort, for much of the existing technology in materials, thermal meteroid garment layup, helmets, visor assembly and connectors would be used.

The current portable life support system weighs 120 pounds on Earth, but only 20 pounds on the moon. As the space suit is improved, such things as an additional battery and water tank can be added to the life-support system to enable the astronauts to remain outside the lunar module for longer periods.

While the current lunar module can remain on the moon's surface for about 36 hours, the initial missions are planned for less than 24 hours. One reason for this is the fatigue limitations of the astronauts, who will have just completed a three-day trip from Earth under less than ideal conditions, and who will face a long journey home.

Lunar module staytime can be increased to three days by including additional water and oxygen tanks, batteries, crew provisions, enlarging the descent propellant tank, and making the crowded quarters more habitable. Since there are no beds, couches, or even chairs in the lunar module, sleeping is difficult.

While the lunar module is on the moon's surface, the command and service module remains overhead in lunar orbit. Some modifications to the basic command and service module would also be required for longer duration missions.

DUAL LAUNCHES

Studies now underway for even more ambitious lunar exploration envision dual launches of the Saturn V. The first launch would place an unmanned payload on the moon and the astronauts would arrive later after launching by a second Saturn V.

Since we would not need to provide for liftoff from the moon for the unmanned payload, we could land an extremely large cargo on the lunar surface. We could provide a shelter for the astronauts, stocked with enough supplies and equipment to sustain a group of explorers for many months. And we could even provide a lunar flying unit, roving surface vehicle, drilling equipment and other items that would permit more extensive geological research.

A lunar flying unit would provide not only greater range of travel over the lunar surface, but would permit vertical mobility for exploration of crater walls and steep terrain.

Another mobility aid under active study is the surface roving vehicle. Using heavy-duty batteries for electrical power, the rover would carry one astronaut over the lunar surface at a top speed of about nine miles an hour on short excursions from the shelter.

REMOTE CONTROL

Before the astronauts leave the moon, they would set the roving vehicle's controls in the mode for remote control from Earth. The remote controlled mode of the roving vehicle will require a radioisotope thermoelectric generator (RTG) for recharging the batteries at regular intervals. The nuclear power supply will be similar to the low wattage "SNAP" units presently being developed for space use. An important consideration will be to use the normally wasted heat associated with the generator for thermal control of the electrical components during lunar night. By allowing sufficient recharge time and selecting a long half-life isotope (PU-238), the roving vehicle can be operated for an extended period of time with a minimum weight and volume for the total power supply sub-system.

By using its television camera and other instrumentation, Earth-based controllers could send the vehicle on automated geological and geophysical trips of more than 500 miles, lasting about one year. During its travels the rover would make scientific measurements of different types of lunar terrain and collect up to 200 pounds of lunar samples. Then it would rendezvous with a manned spacecraft. The crew would transfer the samples to the lunar module, and return them to Earth for analysis.

Lunar exploration interests the scientific community in its search for greater knowledge of the origin and history of the moon and its relation to the Earth and to the solar system. It is also important for learning more about the capabilities and limitations of man as a space explorer. The moon will become a training ground, from which man will some day move on to explore other planets.

Continued exploration will determine the feasibility of the moon as a base for an observatory or a permanent science station, and the possibility of using it as a launch platform or refueling station for planetary exploration.

This latter scheme may not appear very attractive at the moment; however, should water be found on the moon, as either permafrost or crystal water, its prospects would brighten. Should a nuclear reactor be emplaced on the moon in support of lunar surface operations, making possible the conversion of any available water into hydrogen and oxygen by electrolysis, then refueling on the moon for interplanetary voyages may indeed offer advantages.

If our current manned space flight continues to evolve, manned planetary exploration would be feasible during the 1980s. While it will not be necessary to make a firm commitment toward such an objective for several years, the option should be kept open by continuation of unmanned investigations of the planets and the initiation of a large space station program.

No significant modifications to the Saturn V launch vehicle will be necessary to achieve the early lunar objectives. The trans-lunar injection payload capability can be increased 10 per cent by rather nominal first-generation modifications which Marshall Space Flight Center personnel have been considering for some time. Later on, however, the capability of the Saturn V will need to be increased substantially by such means as strap-on solid rocket motors to the first stage. While this approach would give us greater payloads to Earth orbit, we would still need improvements to the upper stages for propelling large payloads to escape velocity. The most effective way for improving the capability of the Saturn V for these distant missions is the addition of a nuclear third stage.

The feasibility and the high performance potential of the nuclear rocket propulsion system have been thoroughly demonstrated in the extensive series of successful reactor and breadboard engine system tests conducted jointly by NASA and the Atomic Energy Commission at the Nuclear Rocket Development Station in Nevada.

The escape payload capability of the Saturn V would be approximately doubled by the substitution of a nuclear third stage for the S-IVB stage now used, which burns liquid hydrogen and liquid oxygen in a single J-2 engine to produce 200,000 pounds of thrust.

Furthermore, studies indicate that there would be no major problem in the integration of the nuclear stage with the Saturn V launch vehicle itself, or with the launch facilities at the Kennedy Space Flight Center.

UNMANNED PROBE

Development of a nuclear stage would not only provide a major advancement in space propulsion capability, but it would give needed flexibility to mission planning. Take an unmanned probe to Jupiter, for example. With a nuclear upper stage for a Saturn V, as compared to a chemical stage, we would have the alternative of sending two or more spacecraft, thereby increasing the probability of mission success; sending a larger single spacecraft; or significantly reducing the duration of the mission. The reduction in trip time is perhaps more important than meets the eye. A 50 per cent reduction in mission duration, which would be possible, would mean reduced operating time requirements for the spacecraft, ground systems, and the people supporting the mission.

The suggested Grand Tour unmanned probe of the planets Jupiter, Saturn, Uranus and Neptune would especially benefit by the use of a nuclear stage. For instance, a Saturn V with a nuclear upper stage could offer a Grand Tour scientific payload of about 40,000 pounds, which would permit individual probes or orbiters to the various planets as the spacecraft flies by. This does not appear possible with chemical rocket propulsion only. A nuclear stage would also open up the launch windows. We are fairly well limited to the 1977–78 window with an all-chemical Saturn V, whereas a nuclear third stage would permit flights in the 1976 to 1980 time period.

A nuclear stage may also prove quite useful for lunar logistics and Earth orbital maneuvering and ferry-type missions. Such possible applications are under study at the Marshall Center.

Manned space flight activities in the immediate post-Apollo period will involve the use of a Saturn launch vehicle upper stage as a Workshop, the progenitor of a

large space station. The 10,000-cubic-foot liquid hydrogen tank of an S-IVB stage, launched into orbit, will be
outfitted as a base where astronauts will perform experiments and make observations during missions of 28 and
56 days. An important part of the 56-day mission, scheduled for 1972, will be the linking to the Workshop of a
large solar telescope and other instruments for direct
observations of the sun.

NASA has been studying progressively larger space
stations for several years. On the basis of these studies,
we are moving to bypass the intermediate space station,
launch vehicles and logistic craft, and go directly into
the design of a large semi-permanent manned space station and a logistic system for lowering costs by as large
a factor as possible. Contracts for definition of the space
station and the low-cost transportation system were let
this spring.

INITIAL LAUNCH

The station would be built 200 to 300 miles above the
Earth by assembling prefabricated modules launched
separately into orbit. The initial launch could be manned
by a crew of perhaps 12 men. Operations would begin
immediately to accomplish many of the fundamental
objectives of manned space flight. By the gradual addition of other modules, the station could accommodate a
crew of perhaps 50 men by 1980.

The station would be planned for 10 years of continuous operation. This would require high reliability sub-
systems design as well as provisions for maintenance,
repair, refurbishment, replacement of parts and replacement of expendables. Electric power would come from
solar panels or a small nuclear generator.

There are many advantages connected with a space
station large enough to contain both laboratory and observatory capabilities. First, its very size connotes a capability for tremendous electrical power, computation,
and data-handling capacity. Further, as we increase the
number of men aboard a space station, we get a far better
relationship between the experimenters and the operators of the station. In a small base, much of the crew

time is required just to operate the station. As the station gets larger, however, the number of occupants who can perform useful experimental work increases rapidly, while the number of operators does not climb as fast.

SPACE WAREHOUSE

Another advantage of a large base is its ability to serve as a warehouse in space. Such a storage place for spare parts, food, materials and equipment would permit continuous operations for long periods of time without resupply, similar to the Antarctica scientific stations.

Another asset of the large station would be its long lifetime. Long duration plus intensity operations are necessary for amortizing the high initial costs over the total returns.

Now, what are some of the problems related to a large station? First, there is the question of long lifetime for the basic systems. How are you to provide long-lasting equipment without incurring costs of testing and qualification so exorbitant as to make the whole project uneconomical? The approach of accelerated testing may help to solve this problem. And too, we should not overlook the importance of using man's capabilities. The system should be maintainable by man. This is the maintenance concept used here on Earth; now we must learn to apply it to space activities.

Another uncertainty still plagues us with regard to the artificial versus zero gravity requirements. Artificial gravity could be provided by a rotating ward room and experiment facility. The activities planned for the 28- and 56-day Workshop missions will give us revealing insight into more facets of manned operations in zero gravity.

Other crucial areas in the operation of a large space station would be time sharing in flight, radio frequency interference and related inter-actions, and the problems of mechanical couplings, vibration, orientation and translation between different experiments and operations.

The crew of a space station would need to be rotated at three- to six-month intervals, and new experiment packages and modules would be brought up as they became available and could be accommodated by the station workload. A low-cost transportation system is a must if the operating costs of the manned space laboratories and observatories are to be reduced to a level that would permit their extensive exploitation for scientific, technological and economic purposes.

As long as we launch a vehicle once and discard it in the ocean, the process will be expensive. The launch vehicle must be re-usable if costs are to be reduced drastically. NASA is performing studies for a re-usable shuttle that would ferry men and materials between the station and Earth. It would be launched vertically, shed supplementary fuel tanks in flight and land horizontally on a runway adjacent to the launch site. The exact size of such a shuttle has not been determined, but to accommodate a 30- to 50-man station, it should probably carry from 12 to 15 men. In addition, it should carry a considerable amount of cargo, probably 20,000 pounds. If we could manage to transport passengers and cargo into Earth orbit for anywhere between $50 and $10 per pound, the space station would become attractive to a large number of users.

In the fields of basic science and basic research, the space station would be valuable in the areas of astronomy, the physics of fundamental particles, space biology, materials research and many others. In the area of applications, it could contribute to the fields of communications, meteorology, and the observation and management of Earth's resources.

Several of these activities are already in progress using unmanned satellites, but man can have a useful and worthwhile role in the expansion of these programs in the future. Man in space can maintain and repair faulty equipment, replace sub-systems, change experiments and operate instruments as a scientist.

I believe that the discoveries, the advances in technology, and the applications of knowledge which are within our reach during the post-Apollo period of space exploration will far exceed the achievements of our first decade in space, if we but resolve to use the space capability now on hand in a continuing evolutionary manner.

ERNST STUHLINGER

15.   APOLLO: A PATTERN FOR PROBLEM SOLVING

Great adventures which lead to a decisive step in human evolution are not a privilege of the past. Perhaps the greatest step in our recorded history is happening right now: We are witnessing how man reaches out beyond his native planet to set foot on his neighbors in space, the moon, Mars, perhaps Venus and the moons of Jupiter. Again, the spirit of adventure, the almost mystical desire to take a bold new step into the unknown has been the prime mover behind the development of space flight. And yet, there is a very charcteristic difference between this and the earlier human adventures: In the space flight project, the daring spirit of the astronauts who are willing to sail the new ocean of space has been matched by the equally undaunted minds of the engineers who develop the extremely demanding techniques of space flight; of the scientists who apply the most advanced scientific knowledge to solve the technological problems; of the organizers and managers who concentrate the powers of a huge, diversified, and initially incoherent work force on the project; and of the politicians who secure the funding support by elevating the enterprise to the status of a national endeavor.

MANAGING SUPER-PROJECTS

This integration of a variety of activities in government and industry, of diversified efforts by scientists, engineers, managers, politicians and space travelers, in order to accomplish one great objective is perhaps the most important achievement of our space program. It enables us not only to open the doors to a fabulous wealth of new scientific knowledge and of technological progress, but it also helps us to learn the intricacies of managing super-projects of unprecedented magnitude and complexity. The space program is giving us the opportunity of going through this learning process. It has already provided us with the confidence that ambitious super-projects can be accomplished, and that their objectives can even be met within the time and funding schedules originally established. This confidence in our ability to accomplish huge projects with difficult objectives is of immeasurable value at a time which is as full of pressing problems as ours. Let us only think of the plight of urban living with its problems of transportation, smog, social unrest and over-population; or the dangerously growing pollution of water and soil which leads to severe imbalances of life cycles in nature, and to an alarmingly rapid depletion of natural resources. These problems are crying for solutions; in scope and complexity, they surpass any problem which has confronted mankind in the past. The know-how, the experience and the confidence which we are gaining in our space program will be of decisive value in the planning and implementation of projects which must be started soon if we wish to secure a decent living for the generations that follow ours.

TECHNO-SCIENTIFIC IMPACT

It is not possible to assess or even to understand the full significance of the manned landing on the moon at the present time, and to predict all its consequences for human evolution. However, with our present knowledge and our past experiences, we can attempt to analyze the significance of Project Apollo for science and technology.

The moon, as our closest neighbor in the universe, has been the subject of studies by astronomers as long as man has been interested in nature. Its distance, its size, its orbital parameters were determined long ago. The questions of its origin, of its evolution, of its internal structure and composition and of its genetic relation with the Earth proved to be far more problematic. When the possibility of space flight began to appear realistic a decade ago, studies of the moon by theoretical and experimental astronomers, by physicists and geologists, chemists and paleontologists, intensified considerably, and a number of very successful unmanned space projects in recent years added a wealth of new knowledge.

For all these studies, the first landing on the moon represents a crowning effort. The men who have been there have observed the lunar surface with an immediacy that remains totally unavailable to the remote observer. Most important of all, they have brought back soil and rock samples from the vicinity of the landing site for investigation by scientist teams with a care and a thoroughness that has probably not been enjoyed by any bit of soil or rock found on the Earth.

LUNAR LABORATORY

In Houston, Texas, the home of the NASA Manned Spacecraft Center, a Lunar Receiving Laboratory has been built. In this laboratory, all lunar samples will be given an initial check before they are sorted and distributed further. Many samples will remain in the Houston laboratory for thorough investigation; the rest will be shipped to the other laboratories which have been selected for sample analysis. This sharing of scientific knowledge with other countries is a most encouraging beginning of international cooperation in space science which will lead to closer contact and better mutual understanding among nations.

First, the nature and composition of the lunar material will be determined by means of chemistry, crystallography, X-ray physics, radiology, petrology and geology. Then the effects of meteoritic impacts will be studied. As long as a piece of rock rested on the surface of the moon, it was exposed to meteorites from space, unprotected by an atmosphere. The meteorite marks were not washed out by erosion, and they should reveal, if properly analyzed and interpreted, a good deal of insight into the actions and roles of meteoritic particles in the solar system. Even more revealing will be the search for cosmic ray action within rock samples. Cosmic rays, in the absence of an absorbing atmosphere, have been hitting the lunar surface since its existence. They accumulated within the rock structure at varying depths, depending on their energies, and some of them even produced nuclear transmutations in the elements of the rock. Their analysis will help us to increase our understanding of the nature of cosmic rays, their composition, their energies, and possibly their variation in the course of geological time. Our observations so far have not given any indication of a magnetic field on the moon. If a field ever existed at previous times, rock samples should still show some effects of magnetization, either as remnant magnetism in ferromagnetic materials or, in case the magnetic fields existed before solidification of the rocks, in the form of an alignment of diamagnetic and paramagnetic molecules along the former field lines.

VESTIGES OF LIFE?

Of very particular interest is the search for any vestiges of life, fossil or recent. Although the likelihood for positive results of this search is not considered great, the possibility of the development of low forms of life during relatively brief periods of a lunar atmosphere cannot be completely ruled out. Even the transfer of spores or other dormant forms of very simple organisms from the Earth to the moon by natural forces has been mentioned as a remote possibility.

In addition to rock and soil samples, the astronauts brought home a large number of photographs, not only of the lunar landscape and of the Earth, but of their footprints, of the dust layer that deposited on the legs of the landing vehicle, of each sample before it was picked, of many rocks and small surface features at close distance, of light effects at the horizon, and of their own movements and actions on the moon. Sorting, analyzing, evaluating and describing all the innumerable details of the moon samples and the moon photographs will certainly result in the desire for more samples and more photographs from succeeding lunar flights.

EARTHQUAKE WARNING

A few simple, but very interesting experiments were set up on the astronauts' first visit. A seismometer equipped with solar cells for electric power is measuring the fine oscillations produced in the lunar crust by the impact of larger meteorites, and also by moonquakes, an indication of geological activities in the interior of the moon, such as volcanism, faulting or tectonic movements. The recordings of the seismometer are transmitted to Earth by radio.

A large area of aluminum foil, carefully checked for scratches and other imperfections, was deployed on the moon. It was designed to absorb and store protons expelled from the sun through space as solar wind. It was also designed to hold cosmic dust and dust thrown up from the lunar surface, to allow micrometeorites to penetrate forming little impact craters, and to collect some cosmic rays. The experiment was prepared by a group of Swiss scientists.

Another entirely passive instrument which does not require attendance or power is an optical reflector. It consists of a large number of small "corner reflectors." Each of them is a pyramid with triangular base and three sides, each side having a right angle at the apex; in fact, each pyramid looks like a corner cut off from a cube. If pyramids of this shape are made of transparent materials or of mirrors, they have a very interesting optical property: any beam of light entering the pyramid through the base returns exactly parallel to the direction in which it entered. The array of corner reflectors placed on the moon by the astronauts are designed to reflect signals modulated into a parallel beam of laser light emitted from an Earth station. The reflected light signals can be observed about two seconds later, from the same station. By measuring the travel time of the signals with high accuracy, the distance between reflector and ground station can be determined accurately. The rate of change of this distance can be measured to a few inches per second, and the fine motions of the moon, such as librations

and oscillations, can be analyzed with corresponding accuracy. Many stations in different countries can independently and simultaneously use the same array of corner
reflectors for such observations.

Even the fine motions of the Earth can be determined
from these measurements with unprecedented accuracy,
particularly the slight variations of the direction of the
Earth's axis known as Chandler Wobble. Several years
ago, it was discovered that abrupt changes in this wob-
bling motion are always followed, a few days later, by
major earthquakes. Hopefully, the corner reflector and
the laser beam signals will help us to develop an early
warning system for earthquakes.

SAND AND PEBBLES

Surprisingly, some of the very fundamental questions
about the moon's past are still unanswered. Was the
moon generated as a "sister planet" along with the Earth,
the two bodies having formed a binary planet system
ever since their joint beginning almost six billion years
ago? Was the moon at first an independent planet,
caught at a later time by the Earth's gravity force? Did
some unknown force even pull the moon out of the body
of the Earth? What caused these fine, meandering rilles
which we can observe on close-up photographs? Quite
obviously, some of them are the remnants of cracks in
the lunar surface. Others, however, look exactly like dry
river beds on the Earth. Could flowing streams of water
have carved them into the loose soil? If so, how could
open water exist in the vacuum that surrounds the
moon? Could perhaps one of the very large impacting
bodies which created the vast maria release such huge
amounts of gases and water that a lunar atmosphere
persisted for a few hundred years? In this case, there
would certainly have been clouds, rain and flowing
water. We will know the answer as soon as our astronauts can go to one of these meandering arroyos. If they
find sand, pebbles or other sediments, ripples or tide-
marks, we know that there must have been water. We

could even imagine that there still exists ice in the form of permafrost at some depth below the surface, at least at places which are never heated up by sunlight. Water is a very abundant by-product of geological activities, and as ice it could persist over very long periods of time in the lunar shadows.

USES OF THE MOON

Will we find ores on the moon? Probably, but it is unlikely that the transportation of these ores or even of their refinement and smelter products back to Earth will be economical. However, the study of lunar ore deposits may prove very useful because it could help us to find and exploit terrestrial ore deposits. The site of the richest nickel deposit known on Earth in the Canadian Sudbury basin is believed to be the edge of an ancient impact crater. Lunar exploration will certainly provide ample information on impact craters, and possibly on ore deposits along the ruins of these craters, and we can use this information to find new deposits on Earth.

The potential use of the moon as a site for astronomical observatories has excited the minds of astronomers for a long time. Visibility would always be excellent because of the absence of clouds, dust, smog and the absorbing and scattering effects even of a clean atmosphere. Telescope pedestals could be firmly mounted, and the slight angular movement of the moon could be compensated in the telescope mount. An object in the sky could be observed for several hundred hours without interruption. These advantages will certainly be utilized as soon as more permanent stations on the moon have been established, particularly also by large-aperture radio telescopes which would profit considerably from the noise-free backside of the moon.

USES OF APOLLO

Travel to the moon is the first step in man's endeavor to expand his domain beyond the confines of his Earth. The next big goal will be Mars, and then other planets

in the solar system. Most of the basic components needed for this interplanetary travel are now in hand. The
Apollo Project has other applications, however. It represents the first step toward permanent, manned stations
in space which permit continuous observations of the
Earth, the sun and the rest of space under conditions
which would never be available from the surface of the
Earth. These observatories, besides their intrinsic value
for astronomy and space physics, will help us to understand the sun-Earth relations, to analyze and predict
weather situations, to survey ocean states, even to search
for natural resources and to assess crop yields. They will
help us to better understand terrestrial processses and
environmental conditions, to predict and even control
hazardous events, and to prevent their tragic consequences.

The huge Apollo Project, with its diversified demands
of advanced technologies, has been an ideal training
ground for engineers and scientists who like difficult assignments with challenging goals. These engineers and
scientists, with all their valuable experiences gained during their Apollo work, are available now, either for other
space projects, or for assignments to projects which may
be less adventurous, but equally demanding of precision,
ingenuity and perseverance: projects of urban renewal,
river decontamination, inter-city traffic, or ocean utilization. Many of these engineers would never have chosen
a technical career had it not been for the challenge and
stimulation of a fabulous project such as the voyage to
the moon.

STIMULUS TO EDUCATION

In times of affluence, and of mental saturation by
movies and television, our young are badly in need of
a stimulant that makes them aware of the high challenge
of science. Physics and astronomy, biology and chemistry
are so highly specialized that they do not appear too
exciting to youngsters unless there is a visible and easily
understandable goal to which these sciences open the
gates. Travel to the moon and to the planets, observing

the stars and galaxies from beyond the "dirty basement window" of the atmosphere, taking an all-encompassing look at our Earth, may well be goals of science which stimulate young people to enroll in college, to work hard, and to become scientists. It is well known from history that those nations which nurtured and encouraged scientific endeavor achieved a better life for their citizens, and a better partnership and co-existence with other nations.

The space program, culminating in the Apollo Project, has become the cutting edge of our technology. Few real innovations in engineering have been made without the pressure of a need. Apollo has created innumerable needs in diversified fields of technology, and the developers and inventors have responded with unprecedented creativity. Never before have the requirements of reliability, accuracy and efficiency been as high as in space projects, and never before has the quality assurance testing for each component been as relentless as in Project Apollo. Each year, an estimated one thousand new technical products and processes, developed for space projects, are made available for civilian consumers. Even after this short period of existence, the space program has become the most prolific source of technical innovations that ever existed.

Perhaps the most profound significance of Project Apollo is its catalytic effect on the material support of large efforts with purely scientific goals. The exploration of space is one facet of man's endeavor to learn more about his environment; to know more about the mysteries of nature; to acquire, in a physical, mental, and spiritual sense, more of the world in which he is living. This endeavor has been the best part of man ever since he existed; it is the driving force behind his evolution.

SIDNEY STERNBERG

16. AUTOMATIC CHECKOUT EQUIPMENT—THE APOLLO HIPPOCRATES

The digital computer in its application as an automatic checkout system for the Saturn/Apollo program was a critical tool in the United States' program to land man on the moon in this decade. Saturn/Apollo weighs 3,000 tons and towers 364 feet above the ground. The vehicle and command module have more than eight million parts. Even with the diagnostic or checkout computers that monitor each step in the sequence from assembly to launch, it still takes 100 engineers and 10 miles of tape, storing more than 2.5 million words, to ensure that the Saturn/Apollo system is ready for launch.

Without automatic checkout equipment, Saturn/Apollo would be a twentieth century Tower of Babel with 500 men (a conservative estimate) attempting to check each subsystem and to communicate their findings in sufficient time to ensure that each system was working in concert with every other system. There would not only be lack of space for the swarm of technicians required to check the system manually, but the communications, logging and correlation of data would be impossible.

The Saturn Ground Computer Checkout system tests 2,700 discrete signals and computes a total picture of the overall health of the vehicle at the rate of 150,000 signals a minute. Two checkout computers perform tests simultaneously talking back and forth, comparing the results of their tests, and displaying the information at checkout consoles for man to review. Four man-years of computational work are done in the relatively few hours of countdown before launch. The results, free from random deviation, are accurate and reliable within the program set up by human design.

During certain parts of the Saturn/Apollo test, it is necessary to clear the launch pad of personnel for safety reasons. Even then, the Saturn Ground Computer Checkout systems (two working in parallel) still do their job of checking out the launch vehicle and reporting its health back to the engineers and managers who in the end must make the final decision that all systems are "go."

Dr. Wernher von Braun, Director of the Marshall Space Flight Center and a pioneer in the exploration of space, volunteered after Apollo 4 that the spectacular success of the mission was due in large part to automatic checkout. "Our success," he said, "has a great deal to do with the methods we are using. I personally attribute, as far as the launch vehicle is concerned, the greatest reason [for success] in this field to our automatic checkout procedure . . . We have a much greater assurance that we won't launch a rocket with anything sick in the system."

The discovery and the prevention of sickness in our increasingly complex systems has become a prerequisite to continued progress. Much of the diagnostic checkout developed in the last 20 years and proven at Cape Kennedy on the Saturn/Apollo program is applicable to our defense, industrial and consumer-oriented systems, and in some instances is absolutely essential. We can expect to see the techniques developed at Cape Kennedy appearing ever more prominently in our daily lives to ensure our convenience and our safety.

COMPUTER DIAGNOSIS

On the Saturn/Apollo project, 19 separate computer programs are used by the RCA Ground Computer Checkout system to diagnose Saturn's health, not only in the few days before launch but at such upstream assembly and test facilities as the Mississippi Test Facility and the Marshall Space Flight Center in Huntsville. These computer diagnostic checkout systems are "up" or operating an average of 324 hours per month. The results of the extensive pre-launch testing are used to check the health of a specific missile and for improving system design and operation. The improvements are made on the missile under test and on those in inventory and manufacture.

There are 18 separate pieces of digital equipment in each Saturn Ground Computer Checkout system. This equipment and the test engineers form a chain of command that continuously monitors the health of the system from conception through assembly to launch. The final check takes place in the few days of launch countdown. During this around-the-clock preparation, there are built-in "holds" for repair of any systems that are not operating to specified requirements. During the countdown which lasts 80 hours or more, the Saturn Ground Computer Checkout system continuously retests every system that it has tested many times before. These tests are dynamic or real. Moreover, the systems or sub-systems are checked out in relation with other systems and sub-systems working dynamically. As all of us know, it is one thing to test a radio tube in a vacuum tube tester and quite another thing to test it in a radio. A "good" tube in the tester may not be quite good enough in its operating environment.

The Saturn Ground Computer Checkout system checks valves, transistors, microelectronics, miles and miles of wiring, transducers, and all of the other movable and non-movable parts and circuitry, in a real situation with each part operating on conjunction with all of the other eight million parts.

DEVELOPMENT OF EQUIPMENT

The 19 computer programs for the pre-launch check of Saturn V basically model every major system in Saturn, such as propellant utilization and flight control. When the tests are being run, stimuli are applied to the built-in testpoints of the system. The diagnostic equipment does very much what a doctor does when he checks our reflexes for knee-jerk: it taps Saturn's many knees and then compares the reaction to the standards written by the system and design engineers. It also passes the information on to the test engineers, stores it for further evaluation and, in the end, uses all of the accumulated intelligence to identify, with the help of the test engineers, what component is wrong if Saturn's response isn't quite right.

The design of automatic checkout or computer-controlled diagnostic equipment is relatively new. We have always tested our systems and equipment, of course. I suppose the brighter cavemen tried out their throwing rocks before getting into a battle where their food or life might be dependent on the balance of the stone. But sometimes we have not been able to check our systems except in actual use, because we failed to model the systm or to build in test points. I've always wondered how Perseus felt when he had to depend on an untested mirrored shield to guide his sword hand when he slew Medusa. Even today, more of our equipment and tools than not have no built-in diagnostic system. We still depend in most part on statistical prediction to give us assurance that a system will work when we want it to work. For example, the gun we carry on a deer hunt has no built-in test to tell us that we have a defecitve cartridge in the magazine. Our only assurance that a gun will fire is to buy the best ammunition and keep both gun and ammunition clean. It's been only in the last two years that some automobile manufacturers have incorporated in the braking systems of our cars a test to let us know when our brakes are becoming worn.

Each morning in California, I enter into a very complex system of transportation to get to work. There is no automatic checkout system to tell me whether the system is working or whether it has been overloaded. The vehicle I drive has only a rudimentary system—brake, oil pressure and voltage indicator lights to report status on my automobile—a very small sub-system in the total freeway system. However, the checkout on my vehicle, a component in the freeway system, is far ahead of the non-existent diagnostic reporting on the current status of the highway. The very best we may receive are random and very rudimentary reports from police and radio stations.

The first serious attention given to automatic checkout was in the forties when the exigencies of training large bodies of men and the growth in complexity of weapons and communication systems required us to simplify the test and repair of the systems. We began to build in test points or, at the minimum, to make terminals accessible to our test equipment. We increased the number of indicators that provided us status on some of our communication and transportation systems. However, it was the advent of our giant missile systems that demonstrated that the design of diagnostic systems had to be phased with operational development.

It is not practical or healthy to use a dip stick to measure the propellant in a missile. There has to be some system in our large rockets for continuously and safely monitoring this operation because of the volatile nature of propellants. The very size and complexity of some modern systems have also exceeded the practical limits of man's ability to collect, log and compute the needs of the system manually.

There is no specific point in time when it was fully realized that it was no longer practical to design a large missile system and then design the checkout system. The launch control and automatic checkout system for Atlas was an integral part of the total system. Yet the development of the missile and its checkout system was not exactly time- or system-phased. In the Titan and Minuteman systems, there has been a higher level of integration of operational and checkout design.

MARRIAGE OF SYSTEMS

In NASA's Saturn/Apollo program, the developmental work in the forties and fifties culminated in a marriage of operational and diagnostic checkout systems. From the beginning of the program, as much attention was given to checkout as to the operational system. It is now difficult to say where the operational system stops and the checkout system begins. As Dr. von Braun noted, "We have a greater degree of visibility than we had in the past. Of course, you pay a price for this visibility. The more you know about your vehicle, the greater the likelihood that you do discover something that is not operative and as a result you cannot launch. So it is like the man seeing his doctor every two weeks. Chances are that the doctor by continuously running checks on him will update his evaluation of his diagnosis a lot better than a man that very rarely sees his doctor.

"We have assurance that we don't launch a sick bird. But at the same time, the probability of hitting a red line while we are on the count is vastly increased. For this reason, I think the fact that we were able to launch this thing on time is probably the biggest achievement of them all. Because it shows that in spite of all the knowledge we had about the bird, we had no red line values."

PARALLEL EVOLUTION

Paralleling the development of an increasing awareness that complex operational systems had to include automatic checkout systems was the development of computer technology that made automatic checkout or computer-controlled diagnostic systems as we now know them practical. Without the transistor, developed by William Shockley, John Bardeen and Walter Brattain of Bell Telephone Laboratories, it could well have been impractical to build computers needed for the Saturn Ground Computer Checkout system.

Marriage of operational and computer-driven diagnostic testing has forced changes in managing the development of large systems. At the same time, the development of professional management and such concepts as system engineering were part and parcel, with the transistor, of an ambitious goal in making computer-driven, diagnostic checkout development an integral, practical part of system design.

It is now obvious, however it came about, that the complexity of the equipment required to reach our goals, whether in defense, space exploration, or everyday living, requires system engineering. This phrase or concept is somewhat nebulous. It can mean a little bit of everything from its most far out extrapolation of synergism (the total is greater than the sum of its parts) to oversimplistic use of the term to give respectability to designing a simple black box.

I like to think of systems engineering as a methodology that starts with a good definition of a goal and ends only when the manner of reaching this goal is fully efficient and effective. This definition is not the classical one that is used when one writes a book about "how to do" systems engineering. However, I think that it is a useful definition when we are considering what systems engineering does for us. There was a time when equipment and systems were so simplistic and independent that we did not need to give much consideration to equipment interaction with other systems, including the human, in its environment. We could afford the loss of effectiveness because it wasn't very high. This is not true for such systems as Saturn/Apollo. The cost in time and in lives is too expensive if the system is not operating at its full effectiveness.

In designing automatic checkout or diagnostic equipment in conjunction with the operational system, we have recognized that it is not enough just to make a system work; we must have a means of keeping it working effectively. We have integrated within the operational system a method not only of checking it out, but, one which provides a diagnosis. It is not very helpful to have a doctor or a machine that can tell you only that you are sick. This we usually know already. It is much more useful if the doctor or an automatic diagnostic checkout system can tell us what must be done to get well. The ideal, of course, is a program that keeps us and our machines from getting sick. In a very rudimentary fashion, the Saturn Ground Computer Checkout system prevents Saturn, and thus Apollo, from getting deathly ill.

CHECKOUT OF SATURN/APOLLO

Diagnostic testing by the Saturn/Apollo automatic checkout equipment begins as major sub-systems are brought together. At Cape Kennedy, these sub-systems —the various stages of the launch vehicle, the Lunar Module and the Apollo Command Module—are married aboard the mobile launcher in the Vehicle Assembly Building. Beneath the top deck of the mobile launcher is a ground computer checkout system, a sister of the ones that have already checked out the various stages of the launch vehicle in stations across the country. As the major systems or stages are assembled, the automatic checkout system keeps its fingers on the pulse of Saturn/Apollo. At the launch pad, further tests are performed in conjunction with a similar system at the Launch Center. It is this system that has primary responsibility for opening valves, checking and topping off propellant tanks, and testing flight control, stabilization and other systems.

This is how a test works in a typical situation: The test engineer designates the program he wants by typing in the call code on his console keyboard. The computer tells him the present status of the selected program, and when it is stacked and loaded for running. All this is written in plain English on the cathode tube of his display or video data terminal. Also shown are the options the engineer can consider with regard to which portions of the test he wants done. If some selected part of the test requires further breakdown, these too are displayed for his choice.

In the event the computer discovers a programming error or hardware problem, it gives the test engineer a choice of (1) terminating the program and selecting another, (2) going back for another review of his original options, (3) returning to the step which produced the error or (4) disregarding the error and proceeding to the next test step.

For example, if the engineer has selected the test program for the checkout of the propellant utilization system, a discrete signal instruction would be issued by the computer to a potentiometer mounted on the engine mixture ratio valve. The condition of the valve, whether it is open or shut, would be signaled, checked and stored in the computer memory.

As the test is being run, the results are shown on the engineer's display console and recorded in print and on magnetic tape.

THE FUTURE

What about the future in space? In the air? In the home?

Certainly future manned spacecraft which circle the Earth, shuttle back and forth to the moon, and explore our solar system and perhaps others will be complex machines. They will not be able to afford the payload weight of large logistics and repair facilities. They must be designed as superior systems with orders of magnitude increases in time between failures. In addition, they will require continuous diagnostic, real-time, in-flight checkout and repair. As an integral part of the operational system, signal samplers and diagnostic routines will be busy checking the heart, mind and muscles of the vehicle. A mis-operation will be noted, analyzed, reported and recorded. The analyses will include warning and instructions for repair. In the air, the advent of larger commercial aircraft carrying many more passengers and costing significant sums of money for non-flight hours will require similar aids for the flight crews. And in our homes, how convenient it will be to have our television sets and washing machines detect their own problems and automatically place phone calls to our service organizations identifying upcoming problems and replacement parts or repairs required. The NASA Saturn Checkout system with its computer has played a major role in the quest for reliable machine service.